CONTEMPORARY READINGS IN PHYSICAL ANTHROPOLOGY

Alan J. Almquist, Editor

California State University–Hayward

PRENTICE HALL, UPPER SADDLE RIVER, NEW JERSEY 07458

The Library of Congress Catalog Card Number 99-055301

Editorial director: Charlyce Jones Owen
Editor in chief: Nancy Roberts
Managing editor: Sharon Chambliss
Marketing manager: Christopher DeJohn
Editorial/production supervision: Kari Callaghan Mazzola
Electronic page makeup: Kari Callaghan Mazzola
Interior design: John P. Mazzola
Cover director: Jayne Conte
Cover design: Kiwi Design
Buyer: Ben Smith

This book was set in 10/12 Meridien by Big Sky Composition
and was printed and bound by Courier Companies, Inc.
The cover was printed by Phoenix Color Corp.

© 2000 by Prentice-Hall, Inc.
Upper Saddle River, New Jersey 07458

Printed in the United States of America
10 9 8 7 6 5 4 3 2

ISBN 0-13-096269-4

PRENTICE-HALL INTERNATIONAL (UK) LIMITED, London
PRENTICE-HALL OF AUSTRALIA PTY. LIMITED, Sydney
PRENTICE-HALL CANADA INC., Toronto
PRENTICE-HALL HISPANOAMERICANA, S.A., Mexico
PRENTICE-HALL OF INDIA PRIVATE LIMITED, New Delhi
PRENTICE-HALL OF JAPAN, INC., Tokyo
PEARSON EDUCATION ASIA PTE. LTD., Singapore
EDITORA PRENTICE-HALL DO BRASIL, LTDA., Rio de Janeiro

CONTENTS

5 ORIGINS OF MODERN HOMO SAPIENS   123

6 THE FUTURE: PROGNOSTICATIONS AND PREDICAMENTS   171

PREFACE

The story of human evolution is written in the languages of many disciplines. The perspectives that are gained come from disciplines as diverse as paleoanthropology (the study of the actual fossil record), anatomy (both functional reconstructions and comparative), molecular and DNA analyses (the comparing of these substances in living animals), and behavior studies (the comparing of our behavior to that of the nonhuman primates), to name some of the most important contributors. The fact that these studies are at all interesting to individuals beyond the researchers who make the contributions to knowledge can be seen from the attention paid them in the popular press and on television. The immensely popular recent production *Ape-Man*, narrated by Walter Cronkite, is a case in point. Scientists and laypeople alike share an interest in our ancestry, albeit at different levels of sophistication. We want to know where we came from, how long our evolutionary journey took, and what happened to us along the way. Our complete understanding of these facts, while better today than ever before, still remains elusive. It awaits the discovery of more complete fossils from a particular period of time or the observation of the behavior of one, perhaps yet unborn, chimpanzee who may provide new insight into our cognitive nature.

Contemporary Readings in Physical Anthropology offers yet another look at those things that are solved and those that still elude us in the study of human history. This book differs, however, in one significant way from the textbooks that compete for our academic interest: It attempts to summarize the field, present the highlights, and capsulize the debates by using articles taken from the popular press and popular science journals. These articles are, for the most part, written not by the field's experts but by science writers whose careers are dedicated to translating the often arcane and cryptic into texts that at a different level can be enjoyed and discussed by a much wider audience. Among many sources of popular science writing the *New York Times* stands out in terms of ongoing coverage of human evolution and succinct, crisp commentary on the major issues of the day. Though lengthier, articles taken from the popular science magazine *Discover* offer a similar level of analysis but have the added advantage of providing greater detail. Primarily from these sources we offer up in this book what we know (and don't know) about our human history and adaptations, realizing that new discoveries will continue to mold our understanding of the process.

This book is divided into six chapters. Chapter 1 reviews the theoretical considerations and paradigms in the field of human evolution with a summary of the highlights and stumbling blocks that mark it today. Chapter 2 concerns the question of human origins: Where did we come from and when did our unique human trajectory begin? Chapter 3 looks at the relationships between the first human, ape-men (the Australopithecines), and members of our own genus, *Homo*. Chapter 4 investigates questions of human behavior, the roots of human culture, and the use of language in the human adaptation. Chapter 5 attempts to sort out the issues of the origins of modern peoples and their relationships with their more archaic contemporaries, perhaps one of the most challenging (certainly the most argumentative) issues in the field today. While the evolutionary process provides us with little basis for prediction, it is always provocative to speculate as to what comes next. For that reason, Chapter 6 deals with issues that promise to mark our future.

Alan J. Almquist

1

THEORETICAL ISSUES

Trying to understand human evolution has not been easy. The field is marked by contentious debate both among individuals working to find answers to the seemingly endless series of questions and between researchers and those opposed to the very premises on which the research rests. The path has been sidetracked by the well-meaning and the hoaxster, as in the case of the Piltdown forgeries that began to appear in an English gravel pit near London in 1912. Most of the time, however, debate is centered on the interpretation of ambiguous data. Yet it is through such debate that resolution often comes, as Sir Wilfid LeGros Clark noted in his Huxley Memorial Lecture of 1958 entitled "Bones of Contention."

It is an understatement to say that the history of the study of human evolution has proven to be at least as interesting as the bones and stones that give it substance. After the publication of Darwin's *Origin of Species*, which set the theoretical framework for human evolutionary studies, things went downhill fast. Questions emerged for which there were no clear answers. One of the most contentious of the early debates focused on the place of origin for humans. Was it Africa as Darwin believed or Asia as many other researchers believed? Some questions were thought to be resolved. Our original premise of a big-brained early ancestor, bolstered by the discovery of the Piltdown bones, was tainted a few decades later with the discovery of the first small-brained australopithecine by a South African unknown by the name of Raymond Dart. As an idea, a big-brained early ancestor begrudgingly collapsed in the early 1950s when Weiner and Oakley proved Piltdown to be fraudulent. Our understanding of geological time was off by millions of years until the advent of radiometric dating techniques, and, despite Mendel's discoveries of genetic inheritance over 120 years ago, our clear understanding of the intricate workings of the genes remained shrouded in mystery until the deciphering of the DNA code by Watson and Crick only some forty years ago.

Once we agreed that Africa was where the bones and stones of our earliest ancestors would be found, our concept of the age of their fossils was so wide of the mark that when Garniss Curtis finally dated the ash deposits near the site where the Leakeys found *Zinjanthropus boisei* to 1.8 million years, few researchers at the time would believe him. In fact, common wisdom supposed that the human lineage could be traced back in time to a great distance and the race was on to discover the oldest ancestor yet. Leakey himself contributed to this notion with the discovery of successively older species of the genus *Kenyapithecus*, supposedly allied to earlier discoveries in India called *Ramapithecus*. Both these fossils were portrayed as bipeds, even though no postcranial remains had yet been unearthed. Different paleontologists tried to connect Plio-Pleistocene hominids to other creatively reconstructed Miocene and earlier Oligocene supposed ancestors. We didn't abandon this line of inquiry until Sarich and Wilson gave us the "molecular clock" based on the evolution of the blood protein, serum albumin, which focused our search for an ape (read chimpanzee) and human common ancestor somewhere in the 4–6 million year time range.

The question remains: Have we really made progress toward a better understanding of our past? The answer is: I think so, in spite of, or as we could argue, thanks to, the continuing debates in the field. S. L. Washburn summed up the situation aptly when he wrote the following:

> There is no doubt that the human species evolved and that progress is being made in understanding the time, place, and manner of that evolution. But beyond the central fact of evolution and some very general guiding principles, many theories are reasonable; and the fun of evolution comes from trying to show which are the more probable.

That thought in mind, we begin this chapter with Professor Matt Cartmill's look at creationism, multiculturalism, and evolution, which examines some of the current areas of debate about issues peripheral to the field. Evolution is the linchpin of biology. It is the unifying paradigm of all the life sciences. In "Oppressed by Evolution," Cartmill reviews the antievolutionary arguments concocted by the religious right and connects them to new ones offered by the postmodern academic left. After presenting these strange bedfellows he concludes with his own observations about some unsustainable notions that many evolutionists hold.

In regards to current anthropological topics, Glenn Carter Conroy's "Paleoanthropology Today" is a succinct summary of ongoing problems that still require resolution. While the field of paleoanthropology is generally guided by scientific principles and time-honored procedural traditions, these guide-posts of the discipline are sometimes ignored. For example, new taxon (species) may be proposed informally and inappropriately without the use of the rules of zoological nomenclature; data is often illogically (to some of us, that is) interpreted. Conroy points out some other specific instances where there are infractions of the rules and offers some insightful alternative view-points to today's commonly accepted wisdom.

We conclude with a short look at the Piltdown hoax and the new ac-cusations aimed at yet another possible perpetrator. Almost every person who ever came to be involved with the original discovery or interpretation of the Piltdown bones has been figured into somebody's analysis of who was real-ly to blame for the hoax. The primary suspect, amateur paleontologist Charles Dawson, must bear the brunt of most of the suspicions, but did he act alone? New clues discussed by Shanti Menon in "The Piltdown Perp" offer up yet an-other possible conspirator.

DISCOVER

March 1998

Oppressed by Evolution

BY MATT CARTMILL

The Christian right and the multicultural left rarely find themselves united in combat—except when it comes to the holy war against Charles Darwin.

As far as we can tell, all of Earth's living things are descended from a distant common ancestor that lived more than 3 billion years ago. This is an important discovery, but it's not exactly news. Biologists started putting forward the idea of evolution back in the 1700s, and thanks to Darwin's unifying theory of natural selection, it's been the accepted wisdom in biology for more than a hundred years. So you might think that by now everyone would have gotten used to the idea that we are blood kin to all other organisms, and closer kin to great apes than to spiders. On the face of it, the idea makes a certain amount of plain common sense. We all know that we share more features with apes than we do with spiders or snails or cypress trees. The theory of evolution simply reads those shared features as family resemblances. It doesn't deny that people are unique in important ways. Our kinship with apes doesn't mean we're only apes under the skin, any more than the kinship of cats with dogs means that your cat is repressing a secret urge to bark and bury bones.

Yet many people don't accept the idea of evolution, and even feel downright threatened by it. Conservative Christians, in particular, have opposed it; to them, science ran off tack in 1859 when Darwin's *Origin of Species* first hit the bookstores. Over the decades, we biologists have become accustomed to this opposition, but in recent years there has been a change in the antievolution camp. Now we find ourselves defending Darwin against attacks not only from the religious right but from the academic left as well.

In the United States the religious opposition to Darwin is chiefly made up of evangelical Protestants. Some of them are smart, savvy, angry, and well organized, and they have been working here for almost a hundred years to stop biologists from telling people about the history of life. In the early part of this century they persuaded the legislatures of several states to pass laws against teaching evolution. When the courts threw out those laws, the antievolutionists tried a different strategy: fighting for laws giving equal classroom time to "creation science"—that is, Bible-based biology. That didn't work, either. Now they're trying to compel teachers to present evolution as a mere theory rather than a fact. So far they haven't succeeded, but they're still working at it.

It seems clear that these religious antievolutionists aren't going to go away in the foreseeable future; biologists will have to fight them for another century or two to keep them from outlawing Darwin. But if we are to succeed, I think we'll need to give serious thought to our opponents' motives. I suspect they are deeper and subtler than most scientists like to think—or than most crusaders against evolution themselves believe.

One reason I believe this is that the motives publicly claimed by Christian antievolutionists don't make sense. Many will tell you that the evolution issue is a religious struggle between a godless scientific establishment and so-called creationists—that is, themselves. But a lot of evolutionary biologists are creationists, too—devout Christians, Jews, and Muslims, who believe in an eternal God who created the world. They just don't see any reason to think that he created it as recently as 4000 B.C.

Many opponents of the idea of evolution say they reject it because it contradicts the Bible. They claim to believe that every word in the Bible is literally true. But no one really believes that. We all know that when, in John 7:38, Jesus said, "He that believeth on me ... out of his belly shall flow rivers of living water," he didn't mean it literally. It's a figure of speech. Practically every book of the Bible contains some such passages, which have to be read as either figures of speech or errors of fact. Consider Biblical astronomy. The Old Testament depicts the "firmament" as a strong dome or tent spread out above the Earth. It has the sun, moon, and stars set in it—and water up above it, and windows in it to let the water out when it rains (see Gen. 1:6–8, 1:14–17, 7:11, 8:2; Job 37:18; Ps. 104:2; Isa. 24:18; and Mal. 3:10). This is a lovely picture. If you read it as poetry, it's gorgeous. But taken literally, it's just plain wrong. There isn't any firmament or any water above the firmament, and the sun, moon, and stars aren't attached to anything. And if we can all agree that there isn't any firmament, then we can all agree that the literal truth of the Bible can't be the real issue here.

Some religious people say they reject the idea of evolution because it lowers human beings to the level of the beasts and blinds us to the nobility of man. In his closing speech for the prosecution in the 1925 Scopes monkey trial, William Jennings Bryan pointed angrily to a high-school textbook that classed *Homo sapiens* as a mammal. "No circle is reserved for man alone," Bryan protested. "He is, according to the diagram, shut up in the little circle entitled 'Mammals,' with thirty-four hundred and ninety-nine other species of mammals.... What shall we say of the intelligence, not to say religion, of those who are so particular to distinguish between fishes and reptiles and birds, but put a man with an immortal soul in the same circle with the wolf, the hyena, and the skunk? What must be the impression made upon children by such a degradation of man?"

What, indeed? But if you are going to classify living things at all, you have to group people and wolves together in some category, since they are both living things. Actually, the classification that Bryan railed against was in place a century before Darwin published his ideas on evolution. It was the pious creationist Carl von Linn, not some atheistic evolutionist, who named the Mammalia and classed *Homo sapiens* among them, back in 1758. And even then, in the mid-eighteenth century, classifying people as animals was an ancient idea. The Old Testament itself says bluntly that human beings are beasts, and no nobler than any of the others (Eccles. 3:18–21). Yes, of course we are mammals: hairy, warm-blooded vertebrates with milk glands and big forebrains, like wolves and hyenas and skunks. What's so awful about that? What else could we possibly be? Insects? Plants? Seraphim?

Most religious antievolutionists recognize that people resemble animals, but they refuse to believe it's a literal family resemblance. They think it insults human dignity to describe people as modified apes. But the Bible says that God made man from the dust of the ground (Gen. 2:7). Why is being a made-over ape more humiliating than being made-over dirt?

Given such patent contradictions, it seems apparent that there must be something else about Darwinian evolution that bothers antievolutionists. And I think we can get some idea of what it is by studying the strange alliance against Darwin that's emerged in recent years between the forces of the religious right and the academic left.

The academic left is a diverse group. It includes all shades of opinion from the palest pink liberals to old-fashioned bright red Marxists. Probably no two of them have the same opinions about everything. But a lot of them have bought into some notions that are deeply hostile to the scientific enterprise in general and the study of evolution in particular. Although these notions are often expressed in a mindnumbing "postmodern" jargon, at bottom they're pretty simple. We can sum them up in one sentence: Anybody who claims to have objective knowledge about anything is trying to control and dominate the rest of us.

The postmodern critique of science runs something like this: There are no objective facts. All supposed "facts" are contaminated with theories, and all theories are infested with moral and political doctrines. Because different theories express different perceptions of the world, there's no neutral yardstick for measuring one against another. The choice between competing theories is always a political choice. Therefore, when some guy in a lab coat tells you that such and such is an objective fact—say, that there isn't any firmament, or that people are related to wolves and hyenas—he must have a political agenda up his starched white sleeve.

"Science is politics," writes Robert Young, editor of the journal *Science as Culture*. "Recent work has made it clear to those with eyes to see that there is no place in science, technology, medicine, or other forms of expertise where you cannot find ideology acting as a constitutive determinant."

To those who see it through a postmodernist lens, science as currently practiced is pretty bad stuff. Science is oppressive: By demanding that everyone talk and argue in certain approved ways, it tries to control our minds and limit our freedom to question authority. Science is sexist: Designed by males and driven by domineering male egos, it prefers facts to values, control to nurturance, and logic to feelings—all typical patriarchal male hang-ups. Science is imperialist: It brushes aside the truths and insights of other times and cultures. ("Claims about the universality of science," insists historian Mario Biagioli, "should be understood as a form of cognitive colonialism.") And of course, science is capitalist (and therefore wicked): It serves the interests of big corporations and the military-industrial complex.

The scholar Ania Grobicki summed it up this way: "Western science is only one way of describing reality, nature, and the way things work—a very effective way, certainly, for the production of goods and profits, but unsatisfactory in most other respects. It is an imperialist arrogance which ignores the sciences and insights of most other cultures and times.... It is important for the people most oppressed by Western science to make use of what resources there are, to acquire skills and confidence, and to keep challenging the orthodox pretensions of 'scientific' hierarchies of power."

In this view, science is really aiming at a totalitarian control over our lives and thoughts. And though all fields of science are suspect, what most left-wing anxiety centers on is biology. You can get an idea of the fear that pervades this literature—and a taste of the convoluted prose some of these people write—by reading what the philosopher Jean Baudrillard has to say about biochemistry: "That which is hypostatized in biochemistry," he writes, "is the ideal of a social order ruled by a sort of genetic code of macromolecular calculation ... irradiating the social body with its operational circuits.... Schemes of control have become fantastically perfected ... to a neocapitalist cybernetic order that aims now at total control. This is the mutation for which the biological theorization of the code prepares the ground.... It remains to be seen if this operationality is not itself a myth, if DNA is not also a myth."

I don't know exactly what it means to have a genetic code irradiating things with its operational circuits, but it sounds pretty nasty. And Baudrillard isn't the only one who has it in for nucleic acids. Last year in the *Nation*, author Barbara Ehrenreich and anthropologist Janet McIntosh recounted the story of a psychologist who spoke at an interdisciplinary conference on the emotions. When several audience members rose to criticize her use of the oppressive, sexist, imperialist, and capitalist scientific method, the psychologist tried to defend science by pointing to its great discoveries—for example, DNA. The retort came back: "You believe in DNA?"

Why this suspicion of genetics? One reason is its political history. Defenders of privilege have always argued that the people below them on the social ladder deserve their lowly status because they're innately inferior; and scientists who believe this sort of thing haven't been shy about invoking biology to prove it. From the social Darwinists of the nineteenth century, the eugenics movement of the 1920s, and the race-hygiene savants of the Third Reich, down to the psychologists who today insist that social status is determined by our genes, there has always been an abundant supply of rich white male professors gathering data to demonstrate that rich people, white people, and men are biologically superior to everyone else. No wonder genetics is greeted with raised eyebrows and snickers on the left.

But more fundamentally, many people see the biological worldview as a threat to the ideal of human freedom. If people are animals, and animals are machines driven by instinct and conditioning controlled by genes, then the way things are is pretty much the way they have to be. Consequently, trying to transform the world by human action is likely to be a futile undertaking. Those who don't much like the world the way it is—a group that includes most leftwing academics—naturally find this view abhorrent.

As a result, in academic circles outside the natural sciences today, any mention of human genetics is likely to arouse protests and angry accusations of "biological determinism," especially if you mention genes in the same breath as human psychology or behavior. In its extreme form, this left-wing hostility to biology amounts to what Ehrenreich and McIntosh call "secular creationism"—a creed that denies our biological heritage has anything to do with what people want or how they act. "Like their fundamentalist Christian counterparts," they write, "the most extreme antibiologists suggest that humans occupy a status utterly different from and clearly 'above' that of all other living beings."

In North Carolina where I live, we recently saw how this attitude can cause the academic left to line up with the religious right. Last spring the lower house of the state legislature passed a bill requiring that "evolution shall be taught as a scientific theory, not as a proven fact" in the state's public schools. The bill eventually died in the senate. But while it was still on the table, conservative evangelicals lobbied hard for it, local evolutionists lobbied hard against it, and the newspapers were flooded with outraged letters from both sides. At the height of this dustup, Warren Nord, head of the program in Humanities and Human Values at the state university in Chapel Hill, suddenly jumped into the fight on the creationists' side—in the name of multiculturalism.

Darwin's theory, Nord complained, "undermines religious conceptions of design or purpose in nature. As we teach it modern science is not religiously neutral…. [It] conflicts not just with Protestant fundamentalism … but with many traditional Native American, African, and Eastern religions." Nord's conclusion: "If we teach neo-Darwinian evolution and secular accounts of nature in science classes, we must also teach religious accounts of nature…. The only constitutional way to teach students about origins—that is, the only way to be truly neutral—is to let the contending parties (all of them) have their say."

In one sense, there's nothing wrong with Nord's argument. Of course evolution is a theory. We can imagine findings that would cause us to reject the whole idea. But that's just as true for every other big idea in science—and nobody is demanding an equal-time approach to any of the others. There are no bills cooking in America's state legislatures that will order the schools to teach the germ theory of disease and the atomic theory of matter as open questions. That might be an interesting and stimulating approach, but given that, for decades, the evidence that has come in consistently supports these two theories, the schools don't have time for it.

And nobody really wants to see science taught that way. Trying to present all ideas impartially without judging them would mean the end of science education. Like it or not, science is judgmental. It undertakes to weigh all the conflicting stories and find tests that will tell us which one is the least unlikely. If no such tests can be found, then science has nothing to say on the issue.

The idea that people evolved from apes millions of years ago is a testable scientific hypothesis. The idea that humankind was specially created in 4000 B.C. is also a testable hypothesis, and it happens to be wrong. But the idea that Nord and his evangelical allies want to introduce into biology classes—that nature expresses God's purposes—isn't a scientific issue at all, because there's no way to test it. People have been arguing about it for millennia and getting nowhere. The creationists point to all the things in nature that look beautiful, orderly and efficient. The skeptics respond by pointing to other things that look ugly, messy, cruel, and wasteful. The creationists retort that they only seem that way to the finite human mind. Maybe so. But since no tests are possible, all that science can do is shrug.

That shrug is really what distresses the crusaders against science, on both the left and the right. Both camps believe passionately that the big truths about the world are moral truths. They view the universe in terms of good and evil, not truth and falsehood. The first question they ask about any supposed fact is whether it serves the cause of righteousness. Their notions of good and evil are different, but both see the commonplace surface of the world as a veil of illusion, obscuring the deeper moral truths behind everything that gives life its meaning. "Commonsense reality," insists the leftwing anthropologist Nancy Sheper-Hughes, "may be false, illusory, and oppressive.... [We must] work at the essential task of stripping away the surface forms of reality in order to expose concealed and buried truths."

For many people on the academic left, the facts reported by science are just the surface layer that has to be scraped off to expose the underlying moral and political reality. This postmodern approach to facts is a lot like that of the premodern St. Augustine, who wrote in the fifth century A.D. that we should concern ourselves with what Bible stories signify "and not worry about whether they are true."

Science, however, worries only about whether things are true and has no opinion about what they signify. In so doing, it offends both the religious right and the academic left. Both camps reject its claim to being objective and morally neutral. Because they don't think such a thing is possible, they see the pretended objectivity of science as a cover for ulterior motives. The idea of evolution is especially offensive in this regard because it implies that the universe has been value-free through 99.9 percent of its history, and that people and their values were brought into being by the mechanical operations of an inhuman reality. Both the religious and the secular creationists see human life as defined by the moral choices we make. Naturally, they shrink from the biologists' vision of people as animals (since animals don't make moral choices). The right-wingers think Darwinism promotes atheism, while the leftwingers think it promotes capitalism; but both agree it's just another competing ideology, which deserves to be cast down from its high seat of intellectual privilege.

Well, is it? Having offended both the fundamentalists and the postmodernists, I am going to annoy my scientific colleagues by admitting that the antievolutionists of left and right have a point nestled deep in their rhetoric.

Science has nothing to tell us about moral values or the purpose of existence or the realm of the supernatural. That doesn't mean there is nothing to be said about these things. It just means that scientists don't have any expert opinions. Science looks exclusively at the finite facts of nature, and unfortunately, logical reasoning can't carry you from facts to values, or from the finite to the infinite. As the philosopher David Hume pointed out 250 years ago, you can't infer an infinite cause from a finite effect. But science's necessary silence on these questions doesn't prove that there isn't any infinite cause—or that right and wrong are arbitrary conventions, or that there is no plan or purpose behind the world.

And I'm afraid that a lot of scientists go around saying that science proves these things. Many scientists are atheists or agnostics who want to believe that the natural world they study is all there is, and being only human, they try to persuade themselves that science gives them grounds for that belief. It's an honorable belief, but it isn't a research finding.

Evolutionists seem to be especially prone to this mistake. The claim that evolution is purposeless and undirected has become almost an article of faith among evolutionary biologists. For example, the official "Statement on Teaching Evolution" from the National Association of Biology Teachers describes evolution as "an unsupervised, impersonal, unpredictable, and natural process." That pretty much rules God out of the picture. One popular book on evolution, Richard Dawkins's *Blind Watchmaker*, is subtitled *Why the Evidence of Evolution Reveals a Universe without Design*. In his book *Wonderful Life*, Stephen Jay Gould argues that the evolution of human beings was fantastically improbable and that a host of unlikely events had to fall out in just the right way for intelligent life to emerge on this planet. One might well take this as a sign of God's hand at work in the evolutionary process. Gould, however, bends his argument to the opposite conclusion—that the universe is indifferent to our existence and that humans would never evolve a second time if we rewound time's videotape and started over.

But to reach this conclusion, you have to assume the very thing that you are trying to prove: namely, that history isn't directed by God. If there is a God, whatever he wills happens by necessity. Because we can't really replay the same stretch of time to see if it always comes out the same way, science has no tests for the presence of God's will in history. Gould's conclusion is a profession of his religious beliefs, not a finding of science.

The broad outlines of the story of human evolution are known beyond a reasonable doubt. However, science hasn't yet found satisfying, law-based natural explanations for most of the details of that story. All that we scientists can do is admit to our ignorance and keep looking. Our ignorance doesn't prove anything one way or the other about divine plans or purposes behind the flow of history. Anybody who says it does is pushing a religious doctrine. Both the religious creationists of the right and the secular creationists of the left object and say that a lot of evolutionists are doing just that in the name of science—and to this extent they are unfortunately right.

Fortunately, evolutionary biologists are starting to realize this. Last October, after considering several such objections, the National Association of Biology Teachers deleted the words *unsupervised* and *impersonal* from its description of the evolutionary process. To me, this seems like a step in the right direction. If biologists don't want to see the theory of evolution evicted from public schools because of its religious content, they need to accept the limitations of science and stop trying to draw vast, cosmic conclusions from the plain facts of evolution. Humility isn't just a cardinal virtue in Christian doctrine; it's also a virtue in the practice of science.

Paleoanthropology Today

BY GLENN CARTER CONROY

… A short time ago, John Fleagle asked me to write a short essay on what I thought were the "hot issues" or "nonissues" in human evolution these days. My initial response was: What hot issues—haven't we simply been filling in the gaps since Darwin's *Origin of Species?* Didn't the discovery of *Otavipithecus* pretty much solve whatever was left to solve? To some, apparently not! Thus, I offer the following musings and brainteasers for your intellects to munch on. I have had fun thinking about them; I hope you do too. There is more here than meets the eye, so tread carefully. I'd love to hear your answers.

- There is, apparently, no type specimen for *Homo sapiens* (you are nothing but a *nomen nudum*). Therefore, what exactly is "an anatomically modern human?"
- Now let me see if I have this Out-of-Africa story straight. Anatomically modern humans first evolved along the Garden Route of South Africa a little over 100,000 years ago, leaving no archeological trace as to what might have triggered this astounding evolutionary achievement. They then must have quickly left the glorious Cape of Good Hope and quickly marched through the rest of Africa, quickly subduing all the archaic *Homo* in sub-Saharan Africa along the way with their newly evolved mental trigones, since, once again, there is no archeological trace of this event. At this point,

they must have stayed put for a while in order to build up the mtDNA diversity that seems to characterize sub-Saharan African populations relative to Eurasian ones. Then a small mtDNA subset of this group invaded Eurasia and comingled with Neandertals in the Near East for tens of thousands of years before totally wiping them out, as well as everyone else, during the last Glacial period. Now my question is this: If the mtDNA homogeneity in Eurasian populations and heterogeneity in African populations is used as an argument in favor of an African Eve hypothesis, then why didn't this little band of mtDNA Africans also turn south from the Near East, from whence they originally came, and wipe out the genetically diverse African populations they left behind? Am I missing something here?

■ If large-bodied early/middle Miocene apes share many postcranial features with semiterrestrial quadrupeds, and if modern hominoids (apes and humans) share many "hanging" adaptations of the limbs and vertebral column, then just where, when, and how could such "hanging" adaptations have developed just as some of these late Miocene hominoids supposedly were leaving the forests to become bipeds in the expanding Pliocene savannas of Africa?

■ Assuming that the trichotomy among chimps, gorillas, and humans is resolved in favor of chimps-humans, then shouldn't gorillas be used as an outgroup in comparing "hominid" (chimp-human clade) morphological and genetic synapomorphies and symplesiomorphies?

■ Still on the subject of trichotomies: If our molecular friends are right and humans are more closely related to chimps than chimps are to gorillas, then I challenge any reader to come up with a cladogram of craniodental or postcranial features (or both) in humans, chimps, and gorillas that would demonstrate this relationship.

■ A small segment of Neandertal mtDNA apparently doesn't look much like a small segment of modern human mtDNA. Given the fast mutation rate of mtDNA, would any "human" mtDNA from 100,000 to 200,000 years ago resemble that of modern humans?

■ Ted Williams batted 406 in 1941. Thus, using the logic of molecular clock advocates predicting relatively recent divergence dates, we should be able to predict with confidence that when Williams had two base hits in the 1941 season he had been at bat only five times, not counting walks. This would be unlikely. For all we know, he went 0 for 5 his first game and 4 for 5 his second game, or anything in between. His overall season batting average has no predictive value for early season games. The predictive value only increases as one approaches the end of the season. It is only when we are told that he has 200 base hits near the end of the season that we would be fairly confident in predicting that he had been to bat about 500 times.

- Why is it surprising that human mtDNA haplotypes seem so homogeneous? What else could they be? What are the odds that females will beget females who beget females for more than four or five generations? Wouldn't you think the human mtDNA genome must be getting pruned constantly and dramatically every century or so and that mtDNA heterogeneity could only increase in a population if the rate of mtDNA mutation within lineages exceeded that of female lineages dying out? Go figure.

- How many different mtDNA haplotypes are there anyway in the human genome? Do mtDNA haplotypes really coelesce to one individual ("Eve") or to one haplotype that may be found in one, tens, hundreds, or thousands of individuals?

- And speaking of coelesence time, why do some writers keep equating modern human mtDNA coelescence time with the origins of "anatomically modern humans?" Why couldn't human mtDNA coalesce back to early *H. sapiens, H. erectus, Otavipithecus* (my personal choice), or sea cucumbers? Why should the two necessarily have anything to do with one another? Answer: They don't!

- If mtDNA "Eve" was the mother of us all in a mtDNA sense, then who was Eve's mother?

- Let's check a cladogram against a known phylogeny: me, my mother, my grandmother. How do I draw a cladogram of this with the three of us as endpoints? Is my mother more closely related to me than she is to her mother? Perhaps my grandmother was just a hypothetical ancestor? No wonder I wasn't in granny's will.

- Let's assume that Neandertals diverged from the "modern human" lineage 250,000 years ago. Are a Neandertal and a "modern human," each dated to 249,000 years ago, more closely related to one another than the 249,000 year old "modern human" is to a modern human living today?

- Your first molar hasn't changed in size since it first popped into your oral cavity when you were about six years old. I bet your body weight has changed dramatically since then. So has the size of your femoral head, although of course the age of attainment of "adult" femoral head size would have occurred later. So how come regression equations relating first molar size or femoral head size to body weight in fossil hominids (or any primate, for that matter) are used to predict adult body size? Some biologists seem puzzled that intraspecific regression slopes are much lower than interspecific ones. How could it be otherwise?

- The human body or any body can be divided into an infinite number of characters, limited only by the imagination of the investigator. Thus, no matter how large a cladistic character matrix may be, isn't it, by definition, an infinitesimally small part of the organism? How sound are phylogenetic assessments based on infinitesimally small samples? Let's look at it another way. There is no such thing as an independent character: The body is a morphologically integrated whole. Thus, the infinite characters of the human body can be reduced to one. (As the gurus say, we are all one. But I would add, one what?) How sound are phylogenetic assessments based on a sample of one?

- Sciences that, like molecular biology, progress by leaps and bounds, actually force their practitioners to share data by requiring them to publish their raw data in an internationally retrievable way—for example, the base pair sequences of the genomic material used in a study. Wouldn't it be nice if paleoanthropology worked the same way? One argument used by the paleontology community to lambast Sotheby's for its auctioning "Sue" the *Tyrannosaurus rex* for 8 million dollars was that someone could buy it and then hide it away in a locked room so that the scientific community would no longer have access to it. Excuse me, but isn't that what some (many?) of our paleoanthropological colleagues do to the rest of us? Let's see a show of hands. How many of you would like, someday, to study the original fossils of _____ (fill in the blank)? How many of you believe that you will ever get permission to do so in your lifetime?

A major problem in paleoanthropology is that access to and interpretation of its raw material, the fossils, are restricted to a precious few. Thus, I offer for the reader's consideration a call to arms to deal with the situation.

Conroy's Manifesto

1. There should be a statute of limitations on describing fossil hominids and other important primate fossil material. If their discoverers do not publish them within _____ years (fill in the blank), they become fair game for the rest of us.

2. If, after publishing their results, investigators do not share their raw data (e.g., casts, photos, and measurements) with colleagues they should be barred from further taxpayer support (read National Science Foundation), publishing in society journals, and presenting their toys at society meetings. Offenders should also be forced to serve a three-year term as postmodernist film review editors for the American Anthropological Association.

3. The Anthropology section of the National Science Foundation or any interested philanthropic organization should establish and financially

support the paleoanthropological equivalent of a genetic bank. After publication of the descriptions of major fossils, high-quality casts of the fossils should be made. The casts should be deposited and curated in a central repository such as the Smithsonian or American Museum of Natural History (or better yet, Washington University) and be available to all colleagues for study.

4. New hominid taxa should only be described and named in internationally acceptable, refereed journals (no more *H. ergaster* in things like Casopsis SPro Mineralogii a Geologii). The same goes for wholesale taxonomic revisions of well-established, or at least "time-honored," hominid taxa.

5. Species names should be banned as end-points in cladograms. Cladograms do not document evolutionary changes in whole animals or species. Instead, they document only changes in the characters (usually few) under consideration. If there are many characters in the analysis, the numbers of reversals, parallelisms, and so forth become mind-numbing. In other words, stop messing with our heads!

The Piltdown Perp

BY SHANTI MENON

When Charles Dawson, a lawyer and amateur geologist, announced that he had found what appeared to be the partly apelike skull of an ancient human in a gravel bed on Piltdown Common, near Lewes, England, in 1912, it was touted as a long-sought evolutionary "missing link" between apes and humans. But in 1953, chemical analyses of the remains showed that the scientific establishment had been duped for four decades. The cranium belonged to a modern human and the jaw to an orangutan, both skillfully stained and altered to look old. Since then, nearly everyone even remotely connected with Piltdown has been implicated in the hoax. But last May, paleontologist Brian Gardiner of King's College, London, and his colleague Andrew Currant revealed the true identity of the perpetrator. Based on the first solid evidence, Gardiner and Currant conclude it was Martin A. C. Hinton, keeper of zoology at the British Museum from 1936 to 1945.

In 1975 workmen found a steamer trunk bearing the initials M.A.C.H. in a loft at the museum. But its contents were not thoroughly examined until Currant mentioned to Gardiner, ten years later, that the trunk contained a box of bones. Gardiner's analysis showed that the bones had been treated in the same manner as the Piltdown remains—dipped in acid, then stained with manganese and iron oxide. He was looking at Hinton's practice set.

For the last ten years, Gardiner and Currant have been building their case, examining the correspondence of every man involved in Piltdown. Hinton's motivation, they say, was to embarrass Arthur Smith Woodward, keeper of paleontology at the British Museum. Hinton was a museum volunteer at the time of the fraud and had apparently annoyed Woodward by requesting a salary. "Woodward told him to get lost," says Gardiner. "And away went Hinton and concocted the hoax. I don't think he meant it to go as far as it did."

But it did go far; Woodward and others failed to detect a note of whimsy in the Piltdown fossils, which included an elephant femur carved to resemble a cricket bat. "At that time in England," says Gardiner, "we were hoping to find the earliest man. We didn't want the goddamn French or Germans to have it, we wanted it. People wanted to believe it." And once Hinton became a respected scholar, he could not confess, although his entry in Britain's *Who's Who* lists "hoaxes" as one of his interests.

2

Origins of the Human Lineage

After a long debate, the issue concerning the place of human origin was resolved in favor of Africa, vindicating Darwin's long-held view. Following the discoveries of the earliest hominids that were given the curious name *Australopithecus africanus* by their describer, Raymond Dart, in 1924, thousands of fossil bones and hundreds of thousands of stone tools have been recovered from this continent. During the 1970s older fossils called *Australopithecus afarensis* were recovered from sites in East Africa and these were linked directly to the later bigger-brained members of the genus *Homo*. Carefully planned, team-oriented paleontological and archeological expeditions scoured the African countryside for new sites and older fossils—and fossils such as Lucy, the First Family, and the Black Skull made headlines as remarkable finds and became household words. Older yet more enigmatic fossils discovered in the remote deserts of the Afar Triangle, Ethiopia, near the Lucy site, have been called *Ardipithecus ramidus* by team members led by Tim White and Berhane Asfaw. Were these apelike creatures really hominids? Did they walk upright in similar fashion to the later australopithecines? The answers are elusive and await further analysis.

There are many other questions yet to be resolved. What was the paleoenvironmental setting in which the earliest hominids emerged and split from the common ancestor we shared with the chimpanzees? What were the reasons for our unique form of bipedal locomotion? These and other specific questions remain part of the ongoing debate and will be explored in the articles in this chapter.

Much research effort has gone toward solving the question of human origins and the paleoenvironmental setting that spawned the earliest members of our lineage. In this chapter's first reading, "Weather Man," *New York Times* contributor Mark Ridley, a lecturer in the department of zoology at the University of Oxford, reviews a recently published book by Noel Boaz entitled *Eco Homo*. It is Boaz's contention that much of human history was written by the weather, and he puts forth as evidence marked changes in past climates that occur coincidentally with major shifts in hominid development. Ridley offers up some of his own views on this subject.

Discover columnist Kathy Svital takes a more specific look at the causes of paleoclimatic change in "We Are All Panamanians." The Isthmus of Panama, created some 3 million years ago, linked the continents of North and South America for the first time. This land link thousands of miles away from the African home of our early ancestors might also provide us with a link of a different kind. Svital's article offers a provocative explanation as to why fluctuations in the Earth's climate known as the Ice Ages appeared and how they potentially affected the course of human history.

If climatic or environmental change did significantly alter the path of human evolution, what caused what and in what way? In "Sunset on the Savanna," author James Shreeve looks at the problem of the origins of bipedalism, discusses the alternative viewpoints offered by many researchers and concludes that, perhaps, we don't know as much about this adaptation as we thought we did.

In "An Upstanding Ape," Odette Frey addresses the question: Were there other primates not directly related to the hominids who also developed a bipedal form of locomotion? Spanish researchers believe they have found at least one other species that did. If true, these discoveries could lead to the further unraveling of why early humans walked upright.

One of the most recently named fossil species is *Australopithecus anamensis*, recovered from sites located near Lake Turkana in northern Kenya by a team led by Alan Walker and Meave (wife of Richard) Leakey. This species is believed to predate Lucy and her ilk and date around 4 million years ago. *New York Times* columnist John Noble Wilford, in his article "Pre-Humans Stood Up and Walked 4 Million Years Ago, Researchers Say," looks at the evidence for this new species of early hominid and discusses how it might fit into the picture of human evolution.

Differences in size between males and females are called sexual dimorphism. Darwin thought that this feature, common in many species, was the result of sexual selection or mate choice. From studies of fossil humans we know that our earliest ancestors were more sexually dimorphic than we are today. In another *New York Times* article entitled "New Clues to the History of Male and Female," John Noble Wilford examines sexual dimorphism in the human lineage and explains why it might provide important clues for understanding more about the social life of early humans.

Shanti Menon, in "Hominid Hardware," examines stone tools, which provide most of what we know about the technological capabilities of early humans. Yet the more we know about the tool-making abilities of the apes, the more it seems that early humans no doubt used a much wider range of tools than those preserved in stone. The oldest stone tools from the site of Gona in Ethiopia have now been dated to about 2.6 million years ago. Who actually made the tools is the as yet unresolved mystery from this and from a number of other sites in Africa where multiple possibilities exist.

Were our early ancestors hunters, gatherers, scavengers, predators, or prey? In "Death from the Pleistocene Sky," Josie Glausiusz points out that many clues are provided from fossil bones themselves in the form of wounds and puncture marks. In C. K. Brain's illuminating book *Hunters or the Hunted*, leopards featured prominently as successful stalkers of the australopithecines. As a victim of another kind of predator, the famous fossil toddler from Taung offers a glimpse into the life (and death) of our earliest predecessors.

In another Josie Glausiusz article, "Ludwig in the Sky with Diamonds," the possible misdiagnosis of "Lucy's" sex is considered. A video drama portrays a solitary female, bravely struggling with some terminal Pleistocene illness, finally succumbing to it and perishing in the still waters of a lake shore at Hadar. Her preserved remains some 3 million years later are rediscovered by the paleoanthropological team led by Don Johanson, who, inspired by the Beatles song "Lucy in the Sky with Diamonds," gives her the female name "Lucy." Would we have written this scene of death and resurrection in the same way if Lucy was, in fact, a male? Perhaps a young man was actually out for a nightly dalliance and, after consuming too many fermented cranberries, slipped on a wet rock, knocked himself unconscious, and fell into the lake and drowned.

The name Leakey is synonymous with extraordinary accomplishments in the field of human evolution. During her lifetime Mary Leakey may have been overshadowed by her effervescent, dynamic husband, Louis, but her own contributions to the field hold at least equal merit. Mary Leakey was truly one of the great pioneers of African prehistory and she lived a full life, as attested to by her obituaries in the *New York Times*: "Mary Leakey, 83, Dies; Traced Human Dawn," by John Noble Wilford, and "The Grande Dame of Archeology" from the Editorial Desk.

We hear from John Noble Wilford again in the final article in this chapter, "New Analysis of Fossils May Muddy Accepted Path of Human Evolution." While fossils of the species *Australopithecus africanus* from South Africa were the first of the australopithecines to be discovered, in recent years they have been foreshadowed by the better dated fossil hominids from various sites in East Africa. Many new interpretations of the phylogenetic relationships of the australopithecines to early members of the genus *Homo* have left *africanus* side-branched as an ignominious dead end. Wilford reports that two prominent paleoanthropologists, Henry McHenry and Lee Berger, are now challenging that view.

THE NEW YORK TIMES

Sunday, August 17, 1997

Weather Man

By Mark Ridley

Human evolution, the author [Noel T. Boaz] argues, may have been driven by changes in climate. Our ancestors split from the evolutionary lineage that evolved into modern chimpanzees about 5 million years ago. After the split they evolved into australopithecines, and then hominids similar enough to us to be classified as *Homo*: *Homo habilis,* then *Homo erectus* and (maybe a half-million years ago) *Homo sapiens.* They evolved to walk upright on two hind legs; they evolved smaller jaws, bigger brains and, finally (the best evidence begins about 20,000 years ago), a sophisticated culture, with art, magic and religion.

Various explanations have been offered for this series of events: Friedrich Engels thought that modern humans were formed by labor; writing in the 1920s, the Dutch anatomist Louis Bolk thought they came about by "fetalization"—becoming increasingly juvenile in form and behavior; for others, the cause lay in hunting or gathering or tool making. Noel T. Boaz's new book *Eco Homo* argues that human evolution was powered by changes in the environment, particularly by changes in the climate. "This is a long and twisting narrative," he says in the final chapter, "but the consistent theme has been that ecological and environmental changes have had significant and indeed formative effects on human existence and evolution."

To begin with, why did the lineage that contained the common ancestors of both modern chimpanzees and humans split 5 million years ago? One popular hypothesis connects the split with the sinking of the Great Rift

Valley in Zaire and eastern Africa. Those ancestors may have initially strad-dled that region, but as the rift valley developed into an increasing barrier to ape movements, some of the population may have been trapped to the west of the rift, and they evolved into modern chimpanzees. The rest of the pop-ulation was trapped to the east, and they evolved into us.

Boaz, who studies human evolution from the standpoints of both bi-ology and anthropology, gives a fair account of the rift valley hypothesis, but prefers a more original idea of his own. He connects human origins with the "Messinian event"—the drying up of the Mediterranean into a salt basin 5 or 6 million years ago, which probably created the Sahara in what was formerly a forested northern Africa. The crucible of human evolution, Boaz suggests, may have been provided by fragmenting forests in an increasing-ly arid north Africa at that time. This is an unorthodox view. Most anthro-pologists think humans originated in eastern Africa—in Ethiopia, Kenya and Tanzania—where the main early human fossils have been found. Boaz him-self has excavated fossils he thinks may represent human ancestors at a site in Libya. However, he is agreeably fair to his critics—and admits that hard-ly anyone else thinks the fossils are ancestral humans, and that one expert, T. D. White of the University of California, Berkeley, and his students "be-lieve that one of the specimens is from a dolphin, not a hominid."

Eco Homo is written for the educated general reader and has the struc-ture of a narrative; Boaz is more illustrating a viewpoint and suggesting ideas than arguing a case. Skeptical readers can still enjoy it, however, provided they are not too quick to dismiss ideas that have not been proved against alterna-tives. I do not mean that Boaz ignores his critics (indeed the quote from White above shows that he does not), but he prefers to state his position, admit the difficulties and move on, rather than worry the firmest conclusion out of the evidence. I began by thinking, "Well, that's not convincing" on one page and "You don't have evidence for that" on another. But in a field like human evo-lution, where the evidence is fragmentary and the events are unique and lost in the past, it can be a mistake to insist on being convinced. Boaz has origi-nal ideas, and his perspective on human evolution surely contains at least some truth.

The next stage in the narrative, after the human-chimp split, is the ori-gin of bipedality. Here, many anthropologists accept an environmental in-fluence. Walking on two legs may well have evolved in response to a move out of the forests into savanna. Bipedality had evolved by the time of the fa-mous fossil Lucy, who died in Ethiopia about 3.5 million years ago, and Boaz describes good evidence of expanding savanna habitats at the right time (4 to 6 million years ago) and in the right place (east Africa, and possibly north Africa too, if it is relevant).

As the book moves on to the evolution of the large human brain and the origin of culture, Boaz persists with his climatic explanatory frame-work. Natural selection, he argues, favored increased intelligence to deal with challenges posed by climatic fluctuations in ice ages. Culture itself took off in response to the glacial extremes and minimum temperatures of the ice age 20,000 years ago. Well, maybe. It would be more orthodox to look to human social behavior and language for the Darwinian advantage of expanding intelligence and culture. Boaz characteristically makes no attempt to argue with that viewpoint. Indeed, he hardly mentions it.

I think Boaz's paradigm has two main difficulties. One is that climatic explanations look too general for the things that need to be explained. We are trying to explain events that were unique to humans, but every species was experiencing much the same climatic change. That does not rule out an influence for climate, but I am more comfortable with climatic explanations for general changes in many species. Many species move north and south, or evolve smaller and larger body size, or have more or less fragmented ranges in relation to climatic cycles: The fit of explanation and facts looks neater here. Climate does not have the right feel to me for a general theory of distinctly human evolution.

Secondly, there is (as the detective Poirot would say) too much evidence: too much climatic change. Climates are almost always getting hotter or colder or humider or windier or more extreme or more moderate; some climatic change or other will almost always be associated with any evolutionary event. I do not want to sound too anarchic. It is possible to study climatic influences on evolution, but it is not easy. Boaz does not suggest it is. He is aware of the problem, and is at his best when describing the scientific research, which he has contributed to—on chemical isotopes, associated fossils of small furry mammals, and more—that enable us to re-create the environments in which our ancestors evolved. But for all that, Boaz's hypotheses remain not much more than conjectures.

A mean reviewer might portray *Eco Homo* as almost cranky. However, for me it was stimulating and enjoyable to read. Boaz's writing has a pleasant personal touch, particularly when he comes to his experiences in the field, and he has made a large-scale attempt to impose conceptual order on 5 million years of human history. But I do suspect he has exaggerated the importance of the weather in the formative events of modern humanity.

We Are All Panamanians

By KATHY A. SVITIL

When the isthmus of Panama rose from the sea, it may have changed the climate of Africa—and encouraged the evolution of humans.

The emergence of the Isthmus of Panama has been credited with many milestones in Earth's history. When it rose from the sea some 3 million years ago, the isthmus provided a bridge for the migration of animals between North and South America, forever changing the fauna of both continents. It also blocked a current that once flowed west from Africa to Asia, diverting it northward to strengthen the Gulf Stream. Now Steven Stanley, a paleobiologist at Johns Hopkins, says that that change in currents may be behind yet another major event: the evolution of humans. When the isthmus rearranged the ocean, he says, it triggered a series of ice ages that in turn had a crucial impact on the evolution of hominids in Africa.

Stanley's hypothesis, which he describes in a new book called *Children of the Ice Age,* is based on ideas developed by a number of oceanographers over the past decade, notably Wallace Broecker of the Lamont-Doherty Earth Observatory. Broecker has called attention to the climatological implications of a fundamental difference between the Atlantic and the Pacific: The Atlantic is much saltier. The difference arises in part because of the dry trade winds that blow west off the Sahara Desert, evaporating water off the ocean and leaving salt behind. "The trade winds are thirsty, and they pick up a lot of moisture from the Atlantic," says Stanley. "Much of that moisture is carried over into the Pacific and drops into the ocean. So the salinity is quite low on the Pacific side of the Isthmus of Panama, but very high on the Atlantic side."

The result is a global system of ocean currents called the conveyor belt. As salty water moves north in the Atlantic—carried by the Gulf Stream, for instance—it gets colder. The combination of extra saltiness and cold temperatures makes the water especially dense—and especially prone to sinking. In the vicinity of Iceland the salty water sinks to the ocean floor. From there it spreads southward to Antarctica, converges with another sinking current, and loops through the Indian Ocean and into the Pacific. There the water wells back up to the surface and slowly returns to the Atlantic around the tips of South America and Africa.

The entire conveyor belt, the theory goes, is driven by the sinking of water in the Atlantic, and ultimately by the salinity difference between the Atlantic and the Pacific. ("The water of the North Pacific gets just as cold as the Atlantic in winter," Stanley says, "but it doesn't sink, because the Pacific is less salty, and therefore more buoyant.") And before the Isthmus of Panama formed, Stanley argues, the conveyor belt didn't exist. Atlantic water flowed directly into the Pacific between the Americas, reducing the salinity difference. The water that then flowed into the North Atlantic, however, wasn't salty enough to sink into the deep ocean; instead it continued northward to the Arctic. Therein lies the key, in Stanley's view, to how the isthmus may have affected human evolution.

As long as North Atlantic waters flowed into the Arctic, he says, they kept it relatively warm—warm enough, for instance, that marine species from temperate climes, like the blue mussel, could use the Arctic to migrate from the Pacific to the Atlantic. After the isthmus formed, however, the conveyor belt denied the Arctic those warm waters, "and because the sun strikes at such a low angle up there," Stanley says, "it got very cold." Pack ice soon formed, which reflected the sun's rays, chilling the region still further. Soon the influence of the frigid north spread inexorably south, as did the glaciers, and the Ice Age began—a long period of waxing and waning ice sheets from which we have yet to emerge.

The impact of the Ice Age was most strongly felt in the higher latitudes, but it also made Africa colder, windier, and drier. Many researchers have suspected that these changes spurred the evolution of *Australopithecus,* the earliest hominid. As Africa cooled and dried, this school of thought contends, the habitat of *Australopithecus* changed. "Before the Ice Age began, there was probably a very broad zone of open forests on the fringe of the rain forest that was accessible to *Australopithecus,*" Stanley says. When the world cooled off, however, the rain forest shrank, while desert and grassland regions expanded. That's a big problem if you're an australopithecine living a semiarboreal life in a forest habitat. "It must have been a tremendous crisis," Stanley says. *Australopithecus* had to survive on the ground and evolve mechanisms that would allow it to do so. Sometime after 3 million years ago, it branched into two lineages—strong-jawed *Paranthropus* and big-brained *Homo.*

As it happens, there is now strong evidence linking that evolutionary split to a climate change in Africa. The evidence was reported last year by paleoclimatologist Peter deMenocal of Lamont-Doherty, who studied marine sediment cores drilled off the African coast. The cores contain dust blown off the neighboring continent, so they provide a record of how dry it was there when each layer of sediment was laid down—a colder, drier climate made for more dust. Over the past few million years, the African climate has oscillated continually between periods that were relatively cold and dry and ones that were warmer and wetter. But around 2.8 million years ago, the sediment cores show a pronounced change. The duration of the cold-warm cycles increased, from an average of around 23,000 years to 41,000 years. And judging from the increased amount of dust in the sediment, the cold periods got markedly colder and drier.

What's more, says deMenocal, the sediment cores show the same chilling effect two more times in African history—and each time coinciding with a milestone in human evolution. The next change happened 1.7 million years ago—just about when *Homo erectus*, a direct ancestor of humans, appeared. "The colds got colder, the winds got windier, and the dries got drier," says deMenocal. "And then 1 million years ago the duration of these events became longer again—100,000 years instead of 41,000 years—while the colds got colder still, and the dries even drier." At around that time *Paranthropus*, presumably unable to survive a more hostile environment, died out, leaving the field to *Homo erectus.*

The lengths of the individual cold-warm cycles in Africa reflect the influence on Earth's climate of another factor besides the oceanic conveyor belt—the periodic changes in the orientations of Earth's axis that are known as Milankovitch cycles. The axis wobbles like a top's tracing out a circle against the stars every 23,000 years; meanwhile the angle at which it is tilted from the vertical oscillates every 41,000 years, from 21.5 degrees to 24.5 degrees and back. (Right now it is 23.5 degrees.)

DeMenocal's sediment cores suggest that 2.8 million years ago, the tilt cycle took over dominance of the African climate from the wobble cycle—and made the climate more extreme. When the tilt angle is low, less sunlight hits the high latitudes of the Northern Hemisphere in summer, less ice melts, and ice sheets expand. That is just what Stanley says happened when the Isthmus of Panama formed and ocean currents stopped warming the Arctic.

The rise of the isthmus, says Stanley, may have made Earth more susceptible to the tilt cycle and may have conspired with it to allow ice sheets to spread over the Northern Hemisphere. The effects of those ice sheets were soon felt in Africa. "It's a jolting notion of how the human genus evolved," Stanley says. "The uplift of this skinny little neck of land between the Americas set in motion an enormous oceanographic change that allowed the Arctic to cool; that had an enormous effect in Africa, by drying the climate and leading to the evolution of *Homo*. In other words, we would not exist if this little neck of land had not risen up across the ocean from where our ancestors lived."

DISCOVER

July 1996

Sunset on the Savanna

BY JAMES SHREEVE

Why do we walk? For decades anthropologists said that we became bipedal to survive on the African savanna. But a slew of new fossils have destroyed that appealing notion and left researchers groping for a new paradigm.

It's a wonderful story. Once upon a time, there was an ape who lived in the middle of a dark forest. It spent most of its days in the trees, munching languidly on fruits and berries. But then one day the ape decided to leave the forest for the savanna nearby. Or perhaps it was the savanna that moved, licking away at the edge of the forest one tree at a time until the fruits and berries all the apes had found so easily weren't so easy to find anymore.

In either case, the venturesome ape found itself out in the open, where the air felt dry and crisp in its lungs. Life was harder on the savanna: There might be miles between one meal and another, there were seasons of drought to contend with, and large, fierce animals who didn't mind a little ape for lunch. But the ape did not run back into the forest. Instead it learned to adapt, walking from one place to another on two legs. And it learned to live by its wits. As the years passed, the ape grew smarter and smarter until it was too smart to be called an ape anymore. It lived anywhere it wanted and gradually made the whole world turn to its own purposes. Meanwhile, back in the forest, the other apes went on doing the same old thing, lazily munching on leaves and fruit. Which is why they are still just apes, even to this day.

The tale of the ape who stood up on two legs has been told many times over the past century, not in storybooks or nursery rhymes but in anthropology texts and learned scientific journals. The retellings have differed from one another in many respects: the name of the protagonist, for instance, the location in the world where his transformation took place, and the immediate cause of his metamorphosis. One part of the story, however, has remained remarkably constant: the belief that it was the shift from life in the forest to life in a more open habitat that set the ape apart by forcing it onto two legs. Bipedalism allowed hominids to see over tall savanna grass, perhaps, or escape predators, or walk more efficiently over long distances. In other scenarios, it freed the hands to make tools for hunting or gathering plants. A more recent hypothesis suggests that an erect posture exposes less skin to the sun, keeping body temperature lower in open terrain. Like the painted backdrop to a puppet theater, the savanna can accommodate any number of dramatic scenarios and possible plots.

But now that familiar stage set has come crashing down under the weight of a spectacular crop of new hominid fossils from Africa, combined with revelations about the environment of our earliest ancestors. The classic savanna hypothesis is clearly wrong, and while some still argue that open grasslands played some role in the origins of bipedalism, a growing number of researchers are beginning to think the once unthinkable: The savanna may have had little or nothing to do with the origins of bipedalism.

"The savanna paradigm has been overthrown," says Phillip Tobias, a distinguished paleoanthropologist at the University of Witwatersrand in Johannesburg and formerly a supporter of the hypothesis. "We have to look now for some other explanation for bipedalism."

The roots of the savanna hypothesis run deep. More than 100 years ago, Charles Darwin thought that mankind's early ancestor moved from "some warm forest-clad land" owing to "a change in its manner of procuring subsistence, or to a change in the surrounding conditions." In his view, the progenitor assumed a two-legged posture to free the hands for fashioning tools and performing other activities that in turn nourished the development of an increasingly refined intelligence. Darwin believed that this seminal event happened in Africa; where mankind's closest relatives, the African apes, still lived.

By the turn of this century, however, most anthropologists believed that the critical move to the grasslands had occurred in Asia. Though the bones of a primitive hominid—which later came to be called *Homo erectus*—had been discovered on the Southeast Asian island of Java, the change of venue had more to do with cultural values and racist reasoning than with hard evidence. Africa was the "dark continent," where progress was slowed by heat, disease, and biotic excess. In such a place, it was thought, the mind would vegetate—witness the "regressive" races that inhabited the place in modern times. The plains of central Asia, on the other hand, seemed just the sort of daunting habitat that would call out the best in an enterprising ape. In that environment, wrote the American paleontologist Henry Fairfield Osborn, "the struggle for existence was severe and evoked all the inventive and resourceful faculties of man ...; while the anthropoid apes were luxuriating in the forested lowlands of Asia and Europe, the Dawn Men were evolving in the invigorating atmosphere of the relatively dry uplands."

In hindsight, the contrasts made between dark and light, forest and plain, slovenly ape and resourceful man seem crudely moralistic. Higher evolution, one would think, was something reserved for the primate who had the guts and wits to go out there and grab it, as if the entrepreneurial spirit of the early twentieth century could be located in our species' very origins. But at the time the idea was highly influential. Among those impressed was a young anatomist in South Africa named Raymond Dart. In 1925 Dart announced the discovery, near the town of Taung, of what he believed to be the skull of a juvenile "man-ape," which he called *Australopithecus africanus.* While Darwin had been correct in supposing Africa to be the home continent of our ancestors, it seemed that Osborn had been right about the creature's habitat: There are no forests around Taung, and scientists assumed there hadn't been any for millions of years. Forests might provide apes with "an easy and sluggish solution" to the problems of existence, wrote Dart, but "for the production of man a different apprenticeship was needed to sharpen the wits and quicken the higher manifestations of intellect—a more open veld country where competition was keener between swiftness and stealth, and where adroitness of thinking and movement played a preponderating role in the preservation of the species."

In the decades that followed Dart's discovery, more early hominids emerged from eastern and southern Africa, and most researchers concluded that they made their homes in the savanna as well. The question was less *whether* the savanna played a part in the origin of bipedalism—that was obvious—than *how.* Dart originally proposed that *Australopithecus* had taken to two legs to avoid predators ("for sudden and swift bipedal movement, to elude capture"), but later he reversed this scenario and imagined his "killer ape" the eater rather than the eaten, forsaking the trees for "the more attractive fleshy foods that lay in the vast savannas of the southern plains."

Later studies suggested that the environments in eastern and southern Africa where early hominids lived were not the vast, unchanging plains Dart imagined. Instead they appeared to be variable, often characterized by seasonally semiarid terrain, a plain studded with scraggly trees and patches of denser woodland. But no matter: This "savanna mosaic" was still drier and more open than the thick forest that harbors the African apes today. It just made good sense, moreover, that our ancestors would have come down to the ground and assumed their bipedal stance in a habitat where there were not as many trees to climb around in. The satisfying darkness-into-light theme of early hominid development held up, albeit with a little less wattage.

For decades the popularity of the savanna hypothesis rested on the twin supports of its moral resonance and general plausibility: Our origin should have happened this way, and it would make awfully good sense if it did. In East Africa geography seemed to reinforce the sheer rightness of the hypothesis. Most of the earliest hominid fossils have come from the eastern branch of the great African Rift Valley; researchers believed that when these hominids were alive, the region was much like the dry open grasslands that dominate it today. The lusher, more forested western branch, meanwhile, is home to those lazy chimps and gorillas—but to no hominid fossils.

Still, despite such suggestive correspondence, until 20 years ago something was missing from the hypothesis: some hard data to link environment to human evolution. Then paleontologist Elisabeth Vrba of Yale began offering what was the strongest evidence that the drying up of African environments helped shape early human evolution. In studying the bones of antelope and other bovids from hominid sites in South Africa, Vrba noticed a dramatic change occurring between 2.5 and 2 million years ago. Many species that were adapted to wooded environments, she saw, suddenly disappeared from the fossil record, while those suited to grassy regions appeared and multiplied. This "turnover pulse" of extinctions and origins coincides with a sudden global cooling, which may have triggered the spread of savannas and the fragmentation of forests.

Other investigators, meanwhile, were documenting an earlier turnover pulse around 5 million years ago. For humans both dates are full of significance. This earlier pulse corresponds to the date when our lineage is thought to have diverged from that of the apes and become bipedal. Vrba's second, later pulse marks the appearance of stone tools and the arrival on the scene of new hominid species, some with brains big enough to merit inclusion in the genus *Homo*. The inference was clear: Our early ancestors were savanna born and savanna bred.

"All the evidence, as I see it," Vrba wrote in 1993, "indicates that the lineage of upright primates known as australopithecines, the first hominids, was one of the founding groups of the great African savanna biota."

With empirical evidence drawn from two different sources, the turnover pulse is a great improvement on the traditional savanna hypothesis (which in retrospect looks not so much like a hypothesis as a really keen idea). Best of all, Vrba's hypothesis is testable. Let's say that global climate changes did indeed create open country in East Africa, which in turn triggered a turnover of species and pushed ahead the evolution of hominids. If so, then similar turnovers in animal species should have appeared in the fossil record whenever global change occurred.

Over the last 15 years, Andrew Hill and John Kingston, both also at Yale, have been looking for signs of those dramatic shifts at some 400 sites in the Tugen Hills of Kenya. In the heart of the fossil-rich eastern branch of the Rift Valley, the Tugen Hills offer a look at a succession of geologic layers from

16 million years ago to a mere 200,000 years ago—studded with fragmentary remains of ancient apes and hominids. To gauge the past climate of the Tugen Hills, the researchers have looked at the signatures of the ancient soils preserved in rock. Different plants incorporate different ratios of isotopes of carbon in their tissues, and when those plants die and decompose, that distinctive ratio remains in the soil. Thus grasslands and forests leave distinguishing isotopic marks. When Hill and Kingston looked at soils formed during Vrba's turnover pulses, however, they found nothing like the radical shifts to grasslands that she predicted. Instead of signs that the environment was opening up, they found that there was a little bit of grass all the time, with no dramatic changes, and no evidence that early hominids there ever encountered an open grassland.

"Elisabeth's turnover pulse hypothesis is very active," says Hill. "It would have been lovely if it had also been true."

Other research has also contradicted Vrba's hypothesis. Laura Bishop of Liverpool University in England, for instance, has been studying pig fossils from several East African sites. Some of those fossil animals, she has found, had limbs that were adapted not for open habitats but for heavy woods. Peter deMenocal of Columbia University's Lamont-Doherty Earth Observatory has been looking at long-term climate patterns in Africa by measuring the concentration of dust in ocean sediments. Over the past 5 million years, he has found, the African climate has cycled back and forth between dry and wet climates, but the pattern became dramatic only 2.8 million years ago, when Africa became particularly arid. Such a change could have played a role in the dawn of *Homo*, but it came over a million years too late to have had a hand in australopithecines' becoming bipedal.

What may finally kill the savanna hypothesis—or save it—are the hominids themselves. More than anything else, walking on two feet is what makes a hominid a hominid. If those first bipedal footsteps were made on savanna, we should find fossils of the first hominids in open habitats. For almost 20 years, the earliest hominid known has been *Australopithecus afarensis,* exemplified by the 3.2-million-year-old skeleton called Lucy. Lucy had a chimp-size skull but an upright posture, which clinches the argument that hominids evolved bipedalism before big brains. But had Lucy completely let go of the trees? It's been a matter of much debate: Oddities such as her curved digits may be the anatomic underpinnings of a partially arboreal lifestyle or just baggage left over from her tree-climbing ancestry.

Nor did *afarensis* make clear a preference for one sort of habitat over another. Most of the fossils come from two sites: Hadar in Ethiopia, where Lucy was found, and Laetoli in Tanzania, where three hominids presumed to be *afarensis* left their footprints in a layer of newly erupted volcanic ash 3.5 million years ago. Laetoli has been considered one of the driest, barest habitats in the eastern rift and thus has given comfort to the savanna faithful. But at Hadar the *afarensis* fossils appear to have been laid down among woodlands along ancient rivers. Other ambiguous bones that may have belonged to *afarensis* and may have dated back as far as 4 million years ago have been found at nearby East African localities. Environments at these sites run the gamut from arid to lush, suggesting that Lucy and her kin may not have been confined to one particular habitat but rather lived in a broad range of them....

...

At least *afarensis* had enough respect for conventional wisdom to stay on the right side of the Rift Valley. Or it did until last year. In November a team led by Michel Brunet of the University of Poitiers in France announced the discovery of a jawbone similar to that of *afarensis* and, at 3 to 3.5 million years old, well within the species' time range. The ecology where Brunet's hominid lived also has a familiar ring: "a vegetational mosaic of gallery forest and wooded savanna with open grassy patches." But in one important respect the fossil is out of left field—Brunet found it in Chad, in north central Africa, more than 1,500 miles from the eastern Rift Valley, where all the other *afarensis* specimens have been found. This hominid's home is even farther west, in fact, than the dark, humid forests of the western rift, home to the great apes—clearly on the wrong side of the tracks.

In a normal year the Chad fossil would have been the biggest hominid news. But 1995 was anything but a normal year. In August, Meave Leakey of the National Museums of Kenya and her colleagues made public the discovery of a new hominid species, called *Australopithecus anamensis,* even older than *afarensis.* (The fossils were found at two sites hear Lake Turkana in Kenya and derive their name from the Turkana word for "lake.") The previous spring, Tim White of the University of California at Berkeley and his associates had named a whole new genus, *Ardipithecus ramidus,* that was older still, represented by fossils found in Aramis, Ethiopia, over the previous three years. The character of *anamensis* and *ramidus* could well have decided the fate of the savanna hypothesis. If they were bipeds living in relatively open territory, they could breathe new life into a hypothesis that's struggling to survive. But if either showed that our ancestors were upright *before* leaving the forest, the idea that has dominated paleoanthropology for a century would be reduced to little more than a historical artifact.

The best hope for the savanna hypothesis rests with Leakey's new species. In its head and neck, *anamensis* shares a number of features with fossil apes, but Leakey's team also found a shinbone that is quite humanlike and emphatically bipedal—in spite of the deep antiquity of *anamensis:* The older of the two sites has been dated to 4.2 million years ago. And the region surrounding the sites was a dry, relatively open bushland.

This is good news for those such as Peter Wheeler of Liverpool John Moores University in England.... Wheeler maintains that standing upright exposes less body surface to the sun, making it possible for protohominids to keep cool enough out of the shade to exploit savanna resources....

... Alan Walker of Penn State, one of the codiscoverers of *anamensis*, disagrees [with the dry open bushland paleoenvironmental reconstruction]. Though the regional climate may have been as hot and arid back then as it is now, he says, the local habitat of *anamensis* was probably quite different [from today]. Back then the lake was much bigger than it is today and would have supported a massive ring of vegetation. Animal fossils found at the *anamensis* sites—everything from little forest monkeys to grass eating antelope— were lodged in deltalike sediments that must have been deposited by "monstrous great rivers," says Walker, with gallery forests as much as a mile or two wide on both banks.

Even Laetoli is proving to be a mixed blessing for savanna lovers.... In separate studies, [Kaye] Reed [of the Institute of Human Origins] and Peter Andrews of the British Natural History Museum took a more thorough look at Laetoli, and both concluded that the original description was far too bleak. "Monkeys have to have trees to eat and sleep in," says Reed. "I don't want to give the impression that this was some kind of deep forest. But certainly Laetoli was more heavily wooded than we thought."

Ardipithecus ramidus poses a potentially more devastating blow to the savanna hypothesis. The 4.4-million-year-old species has a skull and teeth that are even more primitive and chimplike than *anamensis*. Other traits of its anatomy, however, align it with later hominids such as *afarensis*. It remains to be seen whether *ramidus* is an early cousin of our direct ancestors or is indeed at the very base of the hominid lineage (its name perhaps reveals the hope of its discovers, deriving from the Afar word for "root"). What we do know is that the species lived in a densely wooded habitat along with forest-dwelling monkey species and the kudu, an antelope that prefers a bushy habitat.

"We interpret these initial results as evidence that the hominids lived and died in a wooded setting," says Tim White.

A. ramidus would be the final nail in the coffin of the savanna hypothesis, except for one crucial bit of missing information: None of its discoverers will yet say if it was bipedal. Researchers have unearthed a partial skeleton consisting of over 100 fragments of dozens of bones, including hand bones, foot bones, wrist bones—more than enough to determine whether the creature walked like a human or like a chimp. Unfortunately the fragile bones are encased in sediment that must be laboriously chipped away before a proper analysis can begin....

There are plenty of other puzzling bones to ponder in the meantime. Back in South Africa, where Dart found the first australopithecine, researchers have begun analyzing a horde of some 500 new and previously collected specimens from a site called Sterkfontein. Some of them may have a potent impact on the savanna hypothesis.

The most widely publicized is "Little Foot," a tantalizing string of four connected foot bones running from the ankle to the base of the big toe. Little Foot is between 3 and 3.5 million years old, hundreds of thousands of years younger than the *ramidus* and *anamensis* specimens. Yet according to Phillip Tobias and his Witwatersrand colleague Ronald Clarke, the fossil demonstrates that this early species of australopithecine—quite probably *A. africanus*—still spent time in the trees. While the anklebone, Tobias and Clarke say, is built to take the weight of a bipedal stride, the foot is also surprisingly primitive. This is especially true of the big toe, which they contend splayed out to the side like a chimpanzee's, all the better to grasp tree branches when climbing.

Although not everyone agrees that Little Foot's foot is so apelike, a host of other fossils from Sterkfontein also speak of the trees. Lee Berger, also at Witwatersrand, has analyzed several shoulder girdles from the collection and found them even better suited to climbing and suspending behavior than those of *afarensis*. He and Tobias have analyzed a shinbone from the same site and concluded it was more chimplike than human. And in what is perhaps the most compelling finding so far, Berger and Henry McHenry of the University of California at Davis have analyzed the proportions of arms and legs of the Sterkfontein *africanus* specimens and found that they were closer to chimps than to humans.

...

... [These] South African researchers argue [that] bipedalism was not associated with the savanna. "The idea that bipedalism evolved as an adaptation to the savanna," declares Tobias, "can be thrown out the window."

If so, it shall be missed. For all its shortcomings—a shortage of evidence being the first among them—the savanna hypothesis provided a tidy, plausible explanation for a profound mystery: What set human beings apart from the rest of creation? If not the savanna, what did cause the first hominids to become bipedal? Why develop anatomy good only for walking on the ground when you are still living among the trees? For all the effort it has taken to bring down the savanna hypothesis, it will take much more to build up something else in its place.

...

"We're back to square one," says Tobias.

"Square one" is not completely empty. Kevin Hunt of Indiana University, for instance, has recently revived the idea that bipedalism was initially an adaptation for woodland feeding rather than a new way of getting around. Chimps often stand while feeding in small trees and bushes, stabilizing themselves by hanging onto an overhanging branch. Hunt suggests that the earliest australopithecines made an anatomic commitment to this specialized way of obtaining food.

Nina Jablonski of the California Academy of Science in San Francisco sees the beginnings of our bipedalism mirrored instead in the upright threat displays of great apes. Perhaps our ancestors resorted to this behavior more than their ape cousins to maintain the social hierarchy....

...

"Bipedality is a lousy form of locomotion," says [Owen] Lovejoy [of Kent State in Ohio]. "It's slower and more awkward, and it puts the animal at greater risk of injury. The advantage must come from some other motivating selective force." To Lovejoy, the force is reproduction itself. In his view, what separated the protohominids from their ape contemporaries was a wholly new reproductive strategy, in which males provided food to females and their mutual offspring....

...

... Bipedalism may have been a poor way of getting around, but by freeing the hands for carrying, it would have been an excellent way to bear more offspring. And in evolution, of course, more offspring is the name of the game.

If the savanna hypothesis is barely kicking, it's worth remembering that it isn't dead. While scientists no longer believe in the classic portrait of protohominids loping about on a treeless grassy plain, there's treeless, and then there's treeless. Despite the revisionism of recent years, the fact remains that Africa as a whole has gradually cooled and dried over the past 5 million years. Even if the trees did not disappear completely, early hominids may still have faced sparser forests than their ancestors. Bipedalism may still have been an important part of their adjustment to this new setting.

"We have to be careful about what we call savanna," says Peter Wheeler. "Most savanna is a range of habitats, including bushland and quite dense trees. My arguments for bipedalism being a thermoregulatory adaptation would still apply, unless there was continuous shade cover, as in a closed-canopy forest. Nobody is saying that about *anamensis*."

Unfortunately they *are* saying that about *anamensis's* older cousin, *Ardipithecus ramidus,* in its deep forest home. Which brings us full circle to the business of storytelling. Every reader knows that a good story depends on having strongly drawn characters, ones the author understands well. Rather suddenly, two new protagonists have been added to the opening chapters of human evolution. About *anamensis* we still know very little. But about *ramidus* we know next to nothing. Once upon a time, nearly four and a half million years ago, there was a hominid that lived in the middle of a dark forest. Did it walk on two legs or four? If it walked on two, why?

"The locomotor habit of *ramidus* is crucial," says Lovejoy, who is among those charged with the enviable task of analyzing its bones. "If it is bipedal, then the savanna hypothesis in all its mundane glory would be dead. But if it is quadrapedal, then the old idea, even though I think it is inherently illogical, would not be disproved."

DISCOVER

February 1998

An Upstanding Ape

By ODETTE FREY

Somewhere in Africa about 4 million years ago our earliest hominid ancestors began walking on two legs. Why those first hominids gave up the tree-dwelling ways of apes is hotly debated by anthropologists. But one thing all anthropologists have agreed on is that a bipedal lifestyle made hominids unique among primates. Now, however, two researchers say they have found evidence that a bipedal ape roamed an island in what is now Tuscany some 8.5 to 6.5 million years ago, a time when our own ancestors were still four-footed tree climbers.

"We're not the only bipeds anymore," says Meike Köhler of the Miguel Crusafont Institute of Paleontology in Sabadell, Spain. "For the first time, we can compare ourselves with another bipedal animal." The ape, *Oreopithecus bambolii,* is not in the hominid family tree—it is related to *Dryopithecus,* believed by some anthropologists to be the ancestor of the great apes. Fragmentary fossils of the ape were first discovered 125 years ago near Monte Bamboli in Tuscany. But until Köhler and her colleague Salvador Moyà-Solà undertook a detailed study of hundreds of *O. bambolii* bone fragments warehoused in the Natural History Museum in Basel, Switzerland, no one knew that the ape walked upright.

Besides having an S-shaped spine and the long femur typical of bipeds, the three-foot-tall *Oreopithecus* had an unusual foot for an ape. "It functions like a bird's foot. The toes are splayed out, which strongly increases its stability," says Köhler. Unlike chimpanzees and other primates that occasionally walk upright, *Oreopithecus* seems to have been fully bipedal. However, it was probably not a very fast walker. Where our own foot bones are rigid, well suited for fast walking, those of *Oreopithecus* still had some of the flexibility of a climbing ape's feet. The ape would have shuffled slowly along, but this wasn't much of a problem, because no predators lived on the island.

In the absence of predators, even a slow biped had an edge on other primates. Walking on two legs burns fewer calories than climbing, so *Oreopithecus* probably lived on less food than other island animals. Many animals on the island showed adaptations to a harsh environment. Some antelope-like animals, for example, constantly regrew teeth, enabling them to eat even very coarse food.

Oreopithecus survived for about 2 million years. Ironically, the ape's shuffling gait may have proved its undoing—it would have been easy prey for predators that came to the island during an ice age, when sea levels fell and land bridges formed.

THE NEW YORK TIMES

Tuesday, May 12, 1998

Pre-Humans Stood Up and Walked 4 Million Years Ago, Researchers Say

BY JOHN NOBLE WILFORD

New, more definitive age estimates, combined with the discovery of more fossils, have apparently dispelled lingering doubts that skeletal remains found in Africa three years ago are indeed those of the earliest known human ancestors to walk erect, scientists reported last week.

The discovery in northern Kenya of 38 more fossil specimens, including skull and tooth fragments, has enabled scientists to draw a fuller picture of the ancestral species, *Australopithecus anamensis*.

These pre-human individuals had apelike jaws, teeth and wrist bones, and a small brain. The males were considerably larger than the females, a characteristically primitive pattern of sexual dimorphism that is pronounced among gorillas. But in other aspects, particularly leg and arm bones, the individuals had a more humanlike anatomy that would allow them to walk upright on two legs.

"It just shows you that we don't evolve all at once in every part of our body," said Dr. Alan C. Walker, a paleoanthropologist at Pennsylvania State University, a member of the team reporting the research. "We do it in little bits and pieces like a mosaic."

When the initial findings about *A. anamensis* were announced in 1995, geologists could not firmly establish the age of the sediments in which the fossils were embedded. Questions were raised about their antiquity. Some scientists suspected that the fossils were a mix from two species. The more humanlike specimens, for example, could have come from younger geologic deposits and from a more advanced species than the one represented by the more primitive fossils.

Since then, geologists sifting through volcanic ash at the discovery sites near Lake Turkana extracted enough crystals to conduct a more definitive argon dating analysis. The new tests put the age of the *A. anamensis* fossils at 4.07 million to 4.17 million years old, some 500,000 years earlier than previous evidence of walking on two legs.

"These tests basically remove any doubt that the origins of bipedalism go back well over 4 million years," Dr. Craig S. Feibel, a geologist at Rutgers University, said in a telephone interview last week.

A research team led by Dr. Meave G. Leakey of the National Museums of Kenya in Nairobi reported the new findings in [an] issue of the journal *Nature*. The other members of the team, besides Dr. Walker and Dr. Feibel, were Dr. Carol Ward of the University of Missouri at Columbia and Dr. Ian McDougall of the Australian National University in Canberra.

In the report, the scientists said the fossils "show that this species is demonstrably more primitive than *A. afarensis*," which emerged as early as 3.6 million years ago and previously was the earliest known upright-walking human ancestor. The famous Lucy skeleton, found in Ethiopia in the early 1970s, was a member of the *afarensis* species, which some experts consider the common ancestor of all later species on the human family tree.

The findings should also be critical to research aimed at filling the gap of knowledge about human origins before *afarensis* and after the lineages of modern apes and humans split from their last common ancestor. Genetic studies by molecular biologists put the fateful split at 5 million to 7 million years ago.

THE NEW YORK TIMES

Tuesday, August 26, 1997

New Clues to the History of Male and Female

BY JOHN NOBLE WILFORD

Among other differences more obvious and beguiling, women on average are shorter and weigh less than men, as the most casual admirer must have observed. It is a striking example of what scientists call sexual dimorphism, the phenomenon in many species of male-female physical differences that go beyond those directly linked to reproduction.

Dimorphism in primates is especially pronounced in gorillas and orangutans; the males are almost twice the size of females. Male chimpanzees are about 35 percent larger than females, which may also have been the size difference among Lucy and her kind, the early human ancestors known as australopithecines.

The celebrated Lucy, a fossil female from 3.2 million years ago, was a diminutive adult, 3 feet 7 inches tall and no more than 60 pounds. Another skeleton found in related African fossil beds, presumably that of a male, measured 5 feet 3 inches and 110 pounds. By contrast, modern humans are not only bigger, but their body-size dimorphism has declined. On the whole, men today are only about 15 to 20 percent heavier and 5 to 12 percent taller than women.

That raises a question that has troubled paleoanthropologists for a long time: When and why did sexual dimorphism in humans diminish to the present level? No one knows the answer, but a new study of Spanish fossils shows that the change occurred much earlier than once supposed, well before the emergence of modern *Homo sapiens* or even the Neanderthals.

In an article in the current issue of the journal *Science*, a team of Spanish paleontologists led by Dr. Juan Luis Arsuaga of the Complutense

University of Madrid reported findings showing that the ratio of male-female sizes of Neanderthal ancestors 300,000 years ago was no different from what it is among modern humans today.

"We know for the first time with any confidence the degree of sexual dimorphism in one fossil hominid species, compared with modern humans," Dr. Arsuaga said in a telephone interview. "Before, it was not known because we lacked large enough samples that we were sure belonged to a single population."

The research was based on an examination of a rich fossil lode at the Sima de los Huesos site in the Atapuerca Mountains of northern Spain, near Burgos. It was the second major fossil discovery in the region in the last two years. In 1995, another group of Spanish paleontologists found fossils and stone tools from human ancestors who inhabited the Gran Dolina cavern at least 780,000 years ago, the earliest evidence of European colonization by human ancestors.

Dr. Arsuaga's team collected fossils of at least 32 individuals who occupied another cave there in the Middle Pleistocene geological period. These were the remains of *Homo heidelbergensis*. Scientists consider the species to be ancestors of Neanderthals, the prototypical "cave men" who became extinct about 30,000 years ago, and to share a common ancestor with *Homo sapiens* some half a million years ago.

Many scientists had assumed that Neanderthals and other prehistoric members of the human family tree in Europe had a greater sexual dimorphism than modern humans. After studying the craniums and skeletal bones, the Spanish paleontologists determined that the fossils did not "show an unusual size variation compared with the distribution of samples of the same size randomly generated from large samples of modern humans."

Dr. Erik Trinkaus, a paleoanthropologist at Washington University in St. Louis, said the findings appeared to be valid, though not surprising. His own research has established, he said, no difference in sexual dimorphism between Neanderthals and modern humans. The new study extends that conclusion back to a somewhat earlier time and a different species, *H. heidelbergensis*.

Why does it matter, knowing the degree of sexual dimorphism in human evolutionary history?

Dr. Bernard A. Wood, a specialist in human evolution at George Washington University in Washington, said that a better understanding of body-size variations in human ancestral species should help fossil hunters interpret their finds. Are the differences in the size of skeletons within the range of sexual dimorphism? If so, in the absence of any clearer evidence like pelvic bones, the large adults can be assumed to be male and the smaller ones, female. But if the size differences exceed the determined limits of intraspecies variation, then they are more likely to represent differences in species, not males and females.

Such a controversy has swirled around the Lucy skeleton. She was so small compared with many of the other skeletons lumped in the same species, *Australopithecus afarensis*, which lived about 4 million to 3 million years ago, that some paleontologists argued that the fossils may represent several species, not one.

As it is, Dr. Trinkaus said, scientists are not sure just how dimorphic *A. afarensis* was. As much as chimpanzees—35 percent? So it seems, but the estimate could be skewed by a case of circular reasoning. If they cannot tell otherwise, paleontologists classify all large skeletons as male and smaller ones as female, which could shift estimates of size variation to a higher level of sexual dimorphism.

Because the level of dimorphism has implications for behavior, the knowledge can be the basis for making careful inferences about the social life of ancient ancestors. In living nonhuman primates, for example, those that are highly dimorphic, like gorillas, tend to be polygynous species, not monogamous. Males fight with each other for sexual access to females, and the larger, stronger ones would presumably have an advantage and thus pass on more of their genes to succeeding generations.

While this would have favored the continuation of large males, it presumably would also have tended to produce larger females over time, which has been the long-term trend. Scientists note that the gap in male-female sizes in the human lineage has been closing less as a result of the slight increases in male stature than as a result of the tremendous leap in female size.

"By determining the degree of sexual dimorphism," Dr. Arsuaga said, "we can possibly infer that social aspects of life 300,000 years ago would be more similar to modern humans than we used to think."

Likewise, if scientists could identify the time when dimorphism diminished toward current levels, they might be able to mark the fateful transition in human sexual and family life, when humans began to bond, as a rule, with only one partner. Perhaps then large size ceased to be such an overwhelming advantage for males, and the level of sexual dimorphism began gradually to decline.

Dr. Arsuaga speculated that the transition probably occurred about 2 million years ago with the first *Homo* species that began migrating out of Africa. They were evolving larger brains and making more stone tools. But the few scraps of fossil bones from that time are insufficient to indicate any shift in dimorphism—nothing to match the finds at Sima de los Huesos.

The Spanish paleontologists said they have just begun to investigate the fossil riches there, with further explorations next summer likely to produce more discoveries.

"The fossil record here is so spectacular," Dr. Arsuaga said. "There are probably many more individual skeletons, so many that we can conduct even more detailed aspects of these peoples' lives, their growth, brain development, biomechanics, pathology and nutrition as a species. The sample is so great, it's almost like being able to study a living people."

DISCOVER

May 1997

Hominid Hardware

By Shanti Menon

The oldest stone tools yet found show that our ancestors were slow to innovate; they used the same toolmaking techniques for nearly a million years.

The fist-size chunks of rock that Sileshi Semaw has collected from Gona, Ethiopia, over the past three years aren't much to look at—at least not to an untrained observer. But Semaw, a paleoanthropologist at Rutgers, possesses a highly trained eye, and as soon as he uncovered the first of his rocks he knew he had found something unique. The rocks—he has discovered about 3,000 of them in Gona—were shaped by the hands of human ancestors. And dating from more than 2.5 million years ago, they are the most ancient stone tools ever found.

Primitive hominids banged the rocks together to break off small, sharp-edged flakes for use as cutting and piercing tools. The resulting patterns on the cores, as the larger rocks are called, are unlike anything produced by natural erosion. Dating stone tools of such antiquity is often problematic—their age usually can't be easily determined from surrounding layers of sediments. But Semaw got lucky at the Gona site. Lying on top of the tools was a 2.52-million-year-old layer of volcanic ash, which was reliably dated by measuring the decay of its radioactive elements. And magnetic grains in the rock layer underneath the tools recorded a flip in Earth's magnetic field, called the Gauss-Matuyama transition, known to have occurred 2.6 million years ago. The tools, says Semaw, lay closer to the 2.6-million-year-old layer.

The simple flakes and cores Semaw found, made without much thought as to their final shape, are called Oldowan tools. They're named after Olduvai Gorge in Tanzania, where Mary Leakey discovered 1.8-million-year-old stone tools in the 1970s. Oldowan tools have since been found throughout East Africa, including a recent discovery of some 2.3-million-year-old tools in Hadar, not far from Gona. The tools Semaw discovered, though they push back the origins of the Oldowan industry by some 250,000 years, are practically indistinguishable from those at Olduvai—demonstrating that toolmaking technology remained unchanged for nearly 1 million years.

"Quite a few archeologists believed that ancestral humans who lived prior to 2 million years ago were not as capable as those who lived at Olduvai Gorge," says Semaw. "But the evidence at Gona shows they were capable of making Oldowan tools. And the fact that we found thousands of tools around 2.6 million years ago implies that the hominids who made them weren't novices to toolmaking."

But as to who those hominids were, Gona has yet to offer any clues. Semaw hasn't found any hominid remains at the site. Lucy and other members of her species, *Australopithecus afarensis*, roamed around nearby Hadar 3 million years ago. Researchers have recently discovered a 2.3-million-year-old jawbone at Hadar, which they attribute to an as yet unspecified species of our genus, *Homo*. But not much is known about what came after *afarensis* and before the sketchy early *Homo*. The Gona tools lie smack in the middle of a 700,000-year stretch in the Ethiopian fossil record marked by a paucity of evidence.

Some researchers are nevertheless willing to hazard a guess as to who might have fashioned the tools. Bernard Wood [at George Washington University] suggests that *Paranthropus aethiopicus* (also known as *Australopithecus boisei* or *A. aethiopicus*, depending on whom you're talking to) lived at the right time and in roughly the right place. But Semaw thinks that the tools were fashioned by some undiscovered early *Homo* species.

"*Aethiopicus* has really heavy jaws, built for chewing or crunching almost anything," says Semaw. "But the early *Homo* specimens we have are very lightly built compared with *aethiopicus*." Massive *aethiopicus*, sometimes affectionately referred to as the "Nutcracker," would not have needed tools to break open seeds or bones. But the more slender, delicate early *Homo*, Semaw suggests, would have been motivated to find a better way to process food. Until someone finds hominid remains at Gona, the creators of the world's oldest tools will remain anonymous.

DISCOVER

March 1996

Death from the Pleistocene Sky

By Josie Glausiusz

In 1924, mining blasts at the Buxton limeworks near Taung, South Africa exposed a cavern containing the fossil bones of many small animals—and the 2.5-million-year-old skull of an australopithecine child. Anthropologists concluded that they had stumbled upon the remains of some ancient hominid kitchen and that the "Taung child" had perhaps fallen prey to one of its own kind, "a carnivorous beast," "a shell-cracking and bone-breaking ape." A later theory had a leopard as the culprit. But paleoanthropologists Lee Berger and Ron Clarke of the University of the Witwatersrand in Johannesburg now say an eagle probably ate the child, who was about three and a half years old when killed. Berger first got the idea after seeing a black eagle carry off a vervet monkey. Later he found that puncture marks in baboon skulls scattered beneath eagles' nests—marks made by the birds' talons—were identical to those in the Taung skull. And the small animals found at Taung also implicate a bird of prey. "Our vision of the killer ape has been replaced by our ancestor the hunted," says Berger. "There was no safe moment for our ancestors. They had to watch the skies at every moment."

Ludwig in the Sky with Diamonds

BY JOSIE GLAUSIUSZ

Was our famous australopithecine ancestor "Lucy" really a man? After an-thropologists excavated "her" 3-million-year-old skeleton in Ethiopia in 1974—and named her for a Beatles song playing at the site on the discov-ery day—they soon became convinced it was female. Why? Lucy is small compared with other specimens of *Australopithecus afarensis* found at the same site. But a pair of paleoanthropologists from the University of Zurich have now called Lucy's femininity into question. Martin Häusler and Peter Schmid compared casts of Lucy's reconstructed pelvis with a modern woman's pelvis and the cast of another australopithecine specimen from South Africa. At least 13 of Lucy's features—most notably the promontori-um, a ridge at the rear of the pelvis that makes it heart shaped—say "male." The researchers also found that an australopithecine baby's head probably could not have fit through Lucy's pelvic opening. (The skulls in the two non-human pelves are human baby skulls scaled down to the likely size of an aus-tralopithecine baby's head, of which no fossils exist.) So Lucy may have been male—or a member of an entirely different species. Should her name be changed? Häusler and Schmid suggest Lucifer as an alternative. "Or maybe Ludwig," says Schmid. "But that's too German."

THE NEW YORK TIMES

Tuesday, December 10, 1996

Mary Leakey, 83, Dies;
Traced Human Dawn

BY JOHN NOBLE WILFORD

Mary Leakey, matriarch of the famous fossil-hunting family in Africa whose own reputation in paleoanthropology soared with discoveries of bones, stone tools and the footprints of early human ancestors, died yesterday in Nairobi, Kenya. She was 83.

Her family announced her death but did not give the cause, saying only that she died peacefully.

Over half a century, Mary Leakey labored under the hot African sun, scratching in the dirt for clues to early human physical and cultural evolution. Scientists in her field said she set the standards for documentation and excavation in paleolithic archeology. They spoke of hers as a life of enviable achievement.

"She was one of the world's great originals," said Dr. Alan Walker, an anatomist at Pennsylvania State University who has long excavated fossils with the Leakey family. "Untrained except in art, she developed techniques of excavation and descriptive archeology and did it all on her own in the middle of Africa. It was an extraordinary life."

In a biography of the Leakey family, *Ancestral Passions*, published last year by Simon & Schuster, Virginia Morell characterized Mary Leakey as "the grande dame of archeology."

Beginning in the 1930s, Mary Leakey and her late husband, Louis, awakened the world to Africa's primary place in human origins with their spectacular discoveries and increasingly pushed back the time of those origins much earlier than had been thought. Until then, many scientists still believed the human birthplace would be found in Asia.

She discovered the skull of *Proconsul africanus,* an apelike ancestor of both apes and early humans that lived about 25 million years ago. In 1959, her discovery of a well-preserved skull of a hominid, a member of the extended human ancestral family, brought fame and substantial financial backing to the Leakeys. A few years later, the two Leakeys uncovered the fossils of the first known member of the genus *Homo habilis,* or "able man," in recognition of the many stone tools found among the bones.

From then on, the name Leakey was synonymous with the study of human origins. The flamboyant Louis seemed to know just where to look to find revealing fossils; the envious spoke of "Leakey's luck." Meanwhile, Mary Leakey worked in her husband's shadow, seeing to the plodding excavations and meticulous documentation of their finds.

"Louis was always a better publicist than scientist," said E. Barton Worthington, a fellow of the Royal Geographical Society in London and former African explorer. "Mary was the real fossil hunter."

After Louis Leakey's death in 1972, Mary Leakey overcame some of her natural shyness to assume direction of the family fossil enterprise, which by then one of their sons, Richard, joined as an expedition leader. Her operations centered on Olduvai Gorge and Laetoli, both in Tanzania. On the arid plain of Laetoli, she made her most sensational discovery in 1978: the earliest footprints of a human ancestor.

A Playful Moment, but a Fateful One

As often happens, the discovery of the prints was made by chance—more Leakey luck. While tossing dried elephant dung in a playful camp fight, one scientist on Mrs. Leakey's expedition fell down and saw in the gray surface some curious indentations. They were imprints of raindrops and animals, now hardened to stone and recently exposed by erosion and weathering.

After further exploration, scientists determined that the tracks were made about 3.7 million years ago. The animals had walked over volcanic ash when it was damp from rain, leaving impressions of their feet. The wet ash set like concrete and was later covered over by more ash and silt. There the tracks remained to be found by dung-throwing scientists.

It was two years before a scientist uncovered a heel print that hinted of an even more significant find. It seemed to belong to a hominid. On Aug. 2, 1978, Mrs. Leakey spent three hours examining one of the clearest of these prints. She cleaned the crevices of the print with a small brush and dental pick. All the important elements were preserved: heel, toes and arch. She appraised the print from every possible angle.

Finally, Mrs. Leakey stood up from her work, lit a cigar and announced, "Now this really is something to put on the mantelpiece."

She was at last sure that a hominid had left this print and a trail of prints extending more than 75 feet across the plain. Two and possibly three individuals had walked this way 3.7 million years ago: the larger one, presumably a male; the smaller one, presumably female, and an even smaller individual, perhaps their child, whose prints are sometimes superimposed on the others.

In a Footprint a Clue to Human Behavior

Somewhere along the way, as Mrs. Leakey noted, the female appeared to pause and turn to her left. She might have sensed danger, possibly from a predator or the rumble of a volcanic eruption nearby. Then she resumed her walk to the north.

"This motion, so intensely human, transcends time," Mrs. Leakey wrote in the *National Geographic* magazine. "A remote ancestor—just as you or I— experienced a moment of doubt."

These evocative footprints are the earliest known traces of human behavior. At the time, the discovery established that human ancestors had begun walking upright much earlier than previously thought, long before the evolution of larger brains. Whether upright walking preceded the larger brain, or vice versa, was still a much-debated issue among scholars.

With the discovery of a species called *Australopithecus afarensis*, based on the famous Lucy skeleton, the most likely identity of these prehistoric strollers was established. The species lived between 3.9 million and 3 million years ago, and from the fossils paleontologists have determined that they were as capable of walking upright as modern humans.

"I think it's the most important find in view of human evolution," Mrs. Leakey was quoted by The Associated Press as saying in an interview in September. "I was really looking for tools, but we never found any at the site."

In Stone Age Art, Two Interests Merged

She also looked back fondly on what she called another highlight of her career. She was a budding artist before she met and later married Mr. Leakey, when she turned to fossil hunting and archeology. In 1951, her two interests merged briefly.

Mrs. Leakey recorded on drawing paper some 1,600 of the thousands of late Stone Age paintings in the Kondoa-Irangi region of Tanzania. The work gave her "a great sense of happiness and well-being," she wrote in her autobiography, *Disclosing the Past*, published in 1984, because the drawings afforded a glimpse of the lives of the hunter-gatherers who painted them. "No amounts of stone and bone could yield the kinds of information that the paintings gave so freely," she said.

One of her last books was a collection of these Stone Age drawings, entitled *Africa's Vanishing Art: the Rock Paintings of Tanzania* and published in 1983.

Art and, to some extent, prehistory were part of Mary Leakey's heritage. She was born Mary Douglas Nicol on Feb. 6, 1913 in London. Her father, Erskine Nicol, was a prolific and fairly successful landscape painter, as was his father before him. Her mother, Cecilia Marion Frere, was a descendant of John Frere, a British prehistorian who in 1797 first recognized Stone Age flint implements as primitive tools and weapons.

After World War I, the family spent months each year in Switzerland, France or Italy, where the father painted and took Mary to archeological ruins and the caves painted by Cro-Magnon hunters. As she said, this was the source of her early interest in archeology.

"Basically, I have been compelled by curiosity," she wrote in her autobiography. But formal education was not for her.

Bored by class work and her fellow students, Mary was expelled from two schools and so, with attending a university out of the question, decided to pursue independent studies in drawing and archeology. "I had never passed a single school exam, and clearly never would," she wrote.

At the age of 20, Mary Nicol, a sometime illustrator of stone tools and occasional participant in archeological digs, met Louis Leakey, 10 years her senior, married and an established figure in African archeology with a position at Cambridge University. He asked her to help him with drawings for a book, and she readily agreed. A romance followed, and then scandal.

Scandal in Cambridge Led to Magic of Africa

They would marry as soon as his divorce came through. Meanwhile, they did nothing to conceal the intimacy of their relationship, living together for more than a year in a cottage near Cambridge. This eventually cost him his post at Cambridge, the memory of which was dancing lightly through Mary Leakey's mind years later as she walked up the aisle at Cambridge to receive an honorary doctorate degree.

The two were married in 1936 and set out for Africa, where he had grown up as the son of British missionaries. As Mrs. Leakey wrote later, she was never the same again after "Africa had cast its spell" on her. Much of their marriage was spent at dig sites. "Given the chance, I'd rather be in a tent than in a house," she said in a recent interview with Associated Press.

It was a discovery by the Leakeys in 1959 that, according to Dr. F. Clark Howell of the University of California at Berkeley, marked "the beginnings of paleoanthropology in a modern sense." The pace of exploration quickened. Geologists and anatomists joined the quest, a multidisciplinary approach that the Leakeys did much to promote.

On a July day in 1959, as Louis lay ill in camp, Mary stumbled on some teeth and part of a jaw on a slope of Olduvai Gorge. Rushing back to her husband, she exclaimed, "I've found him—found our man."

How the couple celebrated is not recorded. But in her autobiography, Mrs. Leakey wrote that after an earlier major find they "cast aside care" and that was how their son Philip "came to join our family."

The 1959 discovery turned out to be a 1.8 million-year-old fossil known as the "nutcracker man" because of its huge jaws and molar teeth. It was later designated *Australopithecus boisei.*

As Two Lives Diverged, a New Independence

From 1968 until Louis Leakey's death in 1972, he and Mary Leakey were separated. He spent more and more of his time in the celebrity whirl, raising money and lecturing, while she stuck to her digging at Olduvai. She was becoming more independent, opposing some of her husband's more sensational interpretations of discoveries.

"I ended by losing my professional respect for Louis; and it had been very great indeed," she wrote. "Once that was so I was no longer able to offer the concurrence and unquestioning adulation he now seemed to demand."

Another unsettling episode in her life was the controversy between her and Richard Leakey, on one side, and Dr. Donald C. Johanson, the discoverer of Lucy, on the other. She insisted on the removal of her name from the joint authorship of a paper that made assumptions about the place of the Lucy species in human evolution.

Mrs. Leakey retired from fieldwork in 1983, still smoking small Cuban cigars and accompanied by her beloved Dalmatians. Her honors were many for a woman who never finished high school: medals from the National Geographic Society, the Geological Society of London and the Royal Swedish Academy and many honorary degrees.

She is survived by her three sons, Jonathan, Richard and Philip, all of Kenya, and by 10 grandchildren.

Monday, December 16, 1996

The Grande Dame of Archeology

From the Editorial Desk

Mary Leakey, who died in Kenya last week at 83, was one of the greatest heroes of the heroic age of paleoanthropology. The matriarch of an extraordinary family of fossil hunters, her own discoveries in decades of careful digging in the remote Rift Valley of East Africa helped shape our understanding of the origins and evolution of early humans. Tossed out of two convent schools, without even a high school diploma, she nevertheless won coveted scientific awards and honorary degrees. A shy helpmate to her more flamboyant husband, she went on to equal—some say surpass—his accomplishments.

In the study of prehistoric humankind, fame goes primarily to those dogged enough and smart enough and lucky enough to find crucial fossils. Through a series of striking and well-publicized finds from the 1930s to the present, the Leakey family made their name virtually synonymous in the public mind with fossil discoveries. Mary's husband, Louis, 10 years her senior and married to another when they began an affair, was the best known paleoanthropologist of his day and an exuberant promoter of the field. Their son, Richard, and his wife, Meave, have made important discoveries of their own.

Some think Mary Leakey's own chief find was the discovery in 1959 of a 1.8-million-year-old fossil known as "nutcracker man." The most famous fossil of its day, it triggered an avalanche of field trips that greatly expanded the array of bones and artifacts from which scientists try to deduce the origins and evolution of early humans. Soon thereafter the Leakeys discovered the remains of *Homo habilis*, a toolmaking handyman that was the earliest known ancestor of modern humans. But Mary Leakey was most excited by her discovery in 1978 of a trail of ancient footprints, made by two or three individuals in volcanic ash 3.7 million years ago, which showed that hominids were walking upright far earlier than previously believed. That, she said, was "something to put on the mantelpiece."

The Leakeys had detractors. They were accused of hogging the limelight, misinterpreting some of their finds, occasionally performing sloppy field work. But in a discipline where sweeping theories must be built from scant evidence, it is no surprise to find frequent contention.

The Leakeys' impact was undeniable. Their discoveries offered persuasive evidence that the human family first emerged in Africa, not Asia as previously thought. Their other great contribution was to help make paleoanthropology more interdisciplinary. They brought in geologists, anatomists and other disciplines to help interpret their finds, a trend that has accelerated in recent years as geneticists, climatologists and others have joined the effort to unravel the mysteries of human evolution.

THE NEW YORK TIMES

Tuesday, July 28, 1998

New Analysis of Fossils May Muddy Accepted Path of Human Evolution

BY JOHN NOBLE WILFORD

An analysis of African fossils, including a few new specimens, has revealed a puzzling anatomical difference between two major species of the early human family, one from southern and the other from eastern Africa. The discoverers of the difference suggest that the evolution of the human body thus was more complicated than previously understood, possibly requiring some rearrangement of branches on the family tree.

Writing in the current issue of the *Journal of Human Evolution*, two paleoanthropologists, Dr. Henry M. McHenry and Dr. Lee R. Berger, reported finding that *Australopithecus africanus*, which lived in southern Africa, had more archaic, apelike arms and legs than the earlier *A. afarensis*. That species, which lived between 3.9 and 3 million years ago in East Africa (mostly the nations of Tanzania, Kenya and Ethiopia today) and is best known from the skeleton popularly called Lucy, had more humanlike limbs. Both were capable of upright walking.

"This is not what would be expected from progressive evolution," the scientists said of their findings. Dr. McHenry is a paleoanthropologist at the University of California at Davis, and Dr. Berger is at the University of Witwatersrand in Johannesburg.

The australopithecines included several species of hominids transitional between apes and humans. Since the Lucy discovery in the early 1970s, most specialists in human origins have come to accept the *afarensis* as the likely ancestral species in the lineage leading to the human genus, *Homo*, about 2.5 million years ago.

For Lucy and her kind to evolve into descendants with more apelike limbs, the scientists said, evolution would have to go backward, which rarely happens. One possible explanation for such an evolutionary reversal, they said, might have been to adapt to a more arboreal environment.

In a popular account of the findings in the August issue of *National Geographic* magazine, Dr. Berger said it was more likely that *africanus* did not descend from *afarensis* but that the two species evolved separately. They were apparently "sister species that share a missing-link ancestor."

Thus, only one of them could have been a direct ancestor of humans, Dr. Berger said, and *africanus* seemed more likely to have been that ancestor. It had developed a larger brain and somewhat more humanlike face and teeth than *afarensis*. Although the fossil evidence is scrappy, the first members of the *Homo* genus, *Homo habilis*, appeared to have had long arms and short legs, not unlike *africanus*.

Dr. McHenry agreed that *africanus* appeared to be "close to the ancestor of *Homo*." Throwing down the gauntlet before paleontologists working in East Africa, Dr. Berger said, "That reinforces my own conviction that *Homo* emerged from *africanus* in southern Africa and migrated north."

If *africanus* turned out to be on the main trunk of the family tree, then *afarensis* would be relegated to a dead-end branch, Dr. Berger said, culminating in *A. boisei*, which died out about a million years ago.

The analysis was based on a comparison of more than 100 fossil bones from a limestone quarry at Sterkfontein, South Africa, and arid badlands at Hadar, Ethiopia, where Lucy was excavated. The bones included the skeletons of Lucy herself and a male *africanus*. Dr. McHenry's main contribution was the development of a technique of inferring body weight and the length and diameter of limb bones from an analysis of a tiny fragment of a joint.

Like several other paleoanthropologists, Dr. Eric Delson of the American Museum of Natural History in New York said he found the research "a very intriguing piece of work and thought-provoking," but cautioned that it was too early to be redrawing the family tree. He said the fossil record for *H. habilis* was too scant to tie it to the *A. africanus* lineage.

Dr. Bernard Wood, a paleoanthropologist at George Washington University, said the analysis of joints in determining limb sizes was "quite ingenious, but the results are not earth-shattering." He was not surprised, for instance, that the findings did not appear to fit neatly into a pattern of progressive and linear relationships in evolution.

"My own view is that nature would have carried out many experiments," Dr. Wood said, referring to patterns of parallel evolution in which different lineages could arrive at different stages of development at different times. "We are still only scratching the surface of the complexity of human origins," he said, adding that it was unlikely the ancestor-descendant relationships would ever be reconstructed.

3

EARLY MEMBERS
OF THE GENUS HOMO

The emergence of the genus *Homo* was marked anatomically by bigger brained hominids than the ones that preceded them, the australopithecines. Early members of the genus *Homo* appear in Africa first and then spread eastward toward Asia, reaching that part of the old world as early as 1.9 million years ago. A westward migration into Europe apparently was not attempted until about a million years later. These migrating hominids have been generally considered to be members of the species *Homo erectus*, though an old worldwide spread of this species is now contested. How many species of earlier *Homo* hominids existed is another question pondered by the experts. What was once described as the "muddle in the middle" (referring to the Middle Pleistocene) continues to be so with debate revolving around the number of fossil players (species) that can be legitimately fielded.

Technological advancement has also characterized this stage of human evolution with the appearance of more sophisticated tool types of the well-described Acheulean tradition. These tools, often referred to as bifaces (because flaking is present on two sides of the stone) are found widely throughout the Old World with the exception of the Far East. Lack of Acheulean tools in eastern Asia has suggested to some researchers that *Homo erectus*, best known from this region, also was a side branch in human evolution, ultimately giving way to some more innovative cousin who made his appearance further west.

How old is the genus *Homo* anyway? Part of the answer to this question first surfaced in the early 1960s with the discovery by the Leakeys of fossils in the lower deposits of Olduvai Gorge, which they attributed to a new species, *Homo habilis*. Later fossils were found in other sites in East Africa, and new species names were assigned to them. In addition, fossils recovered in the late 1940s and 1950s from the well-known South African sites of Sterkfontein and Swartkrans were thrown into the pot, raising the list of specimens of early *Homo* to a respectable number. So far, congratulations for the discovery of the oldest specimen of *Homo* go to Don Johanson and the IHO team, as John Noble Wilford of the *New York Times* reports in "2.3-Million-Year-Old Jaw Extends Human Family."

The "muddle in the middle" takes on new proportions with the debate over how far *Homo erectus* ranged in the Old World in terms of both time and space. Once believed to be a species that ultimately invaded the entire extent of this region, occupying it for a period of almost a million years, this notion has been argued against by some researchers who would like to see early African *Homo erectus* placed in a new species *Homo ergaster*, and, additionally, establish the existence of a later contemporaneous species *Homo antecessor*. John Noble Wilford, in "Three Human Species Coexisted Eons Ago, New Data Suggest," reports that at one point during the Middle Pleistocene possibly three separate species co-existed.

To what extent did members of the species *Homo erectus* evolve their technological skills? We once believed from unimpeachable evidence that this species controlled the use of fire, cooking their meat that they had obtained from hunting game. Evidence of supposed hearths found in deposits well inside the Chinese cave site of Zhoukoudian made the best case for this scenario. How unimpeachable this evidence really is is the question taken up by Bernice Wuethrich of *Science* magazine in her article "Geological Analysis Damps Ancient Chinese Fires."

While some researchers are questioning whether *Homo erectus* was as bright as we once thought, others are suggesting that we really don't know the extent of their innovative capabilities. Did *Homo erectus* range further than we thought using modes of transportation we never thought them capable of designing? *Science* writer Ann Gibbons, in her article "Ancient Island Tools Suggest *Homo Erectus* Was a Seafarer," reports on the presence of stone tools on an Indonesian island where tools of the age suggested by the dating shouldn't be.

The latest entry into the competition for species status is *Homo antecessor*. Fossils from the Spanish site of Gran Dolina dated to about 800,000 years are by far the oldest evidence for a human presence in Europe. Never mind the problems in creating a new species to accommodate these fossils; they are important if for no other reason than their great antiquity in this region. The peopling of Europe, it seems, was a more recent event than the migration from Africa that first brought people into Asia. The Spanish finds, however, make it clear that the colonization of Europe was considerably older than we once believed. John Noble Wilford, in his article "Fossils Called Limb in Human Family Tree," describes why some researchers remain reluctant to accept all of the contentions made by the discoverers of these Spanish fossil hominids.

THE NEW YORK TIMES

Tuesday, November 19, 1996

2.3-Million-Year-Old Jaw
Extends Human Family

BY JOHN NOBLE WILFORD

An upper jaw found in the Hadar badlands of northern Ethiopia is being hailed as the most convincing and earliest definitively dated fossil of the genus *Homo*, to which living humans belong.

The 2.33-million-year-old jaw extends the established age of the human family line by 400,000 years, closer to the time of the first evidence of toolmaking and to environmental upheavals that may have been decisive in human evolution. The fossil was found in sediments with a scattering of crude stone tools, the earliest association between *Homo* remains and such artifacts.

Of greatest potential importance, paleontologists said, is the rare glimpse the discovery provides into what has been a kind of dark age of evolutionary change, the period between 3 million and 2 million years ago. Scientists are all but certain that sometime in that epoch the genus *Homo* evolved from the more apelike australopithecines, yet the fossil record in Africa for that period has been frustratingly spotty.

The new discovery was announced yesterday by a team of American, Canadian, Ethiopian and Israeli scientists. A detailed description and interpretation of the fossil is being published in the December issue of the *Journal of Human Evolution*.

Until a skull and other bones are found, however, the scientists said they would not be able to determine the relationship of their find to any of the known *Homo* species, all of which are dated at 1.9 million years ago and later, or whether it is a previously unknown species representing a transitional step. In that case, it might even be a more direct ancestral line leading to modern humans.

In any case, the well-preserved jaw, the researchers write in the journal article, represents "the oldest association of hominid remains with stone tools and possibly the earliest well-dated occurrence of the genus *Homo*." This, they concluded, "promises to add new insights on hominid paleobiology and behavior in this poorly understood time period."

The leaders of the team are Dr. William H. Kimbel, Dr. Donald C. Johanson and Dr. Robert C. Walter, all of the Institute of Human Origins in Berkeley, Calif. Dr. Kimbel is the institute's science director. Dr. Johanson is a paleontologist best known for the discovery in the 1970s at a nearby Hadar site of the "Lucy" skeleton, a 3.18-million-year-old ancestral hominid later designated *Australopithecus afarensis*. Dr. Walter is a geologist who was in charge of dating the jaw, based on an analysis of volcanic ash just above it.

Other paleontologists familiar with the work said the jaw was just what they had long sought to begin filling in the fossil record for early *Homo*.

"The jaw is definitely *Homo* and the date is good," said Dr. Philip Rightmire of the State University of New York at Binghamton. "It's the first good clear confirmation of *Homo* earlier than 2 million years ago."

In recent years, paleontologists had found possible *Homo* traces this old or slightly older in Kenya and Malawi, though most scientists were unconvinced. They were not sure that the three-inch skull fragment from Kenya was from an early *Homo* or an australopithecine. The date for the jaw from Malawi was not well established.

Dr. Andrew Hill, a Yale University paleontologist, who identified the Kenya fragment as a 2.4-million-year-old *Homo*, said: "It's nice to have another specimen and from another part of the anatomy. I think we now know *Homo* existed probably as early as 2.5 million years ago."

Like other scientists, Dr. Nicholas Toth of Indiana University, who specializes in early stone tools, said the discovery did not answer the question of whether the making and use of stone tools began only after the emergence of the larger-brained *Homo* genus or was also a talent of the australopithecines that existed then. Since the earliest evidence of tools is dated at 2.6 million years ago, he said, it is possible that small-brained hominids were the first toolmakers, with brain expansion coming later as one consequence of stone technology.

Members of the discovery team said they could not say with assurance that the stone flakes and chopping tools found at the Hadar site were made by the *Homo* species represented by the jaw.

Ethiopian fossil hunters made the discovery on the first day of their field season in November 1994. They spotted two halves of a maxilla, or upper jaw, that had eroded out of the side of a barren hill near a dry stream bed.

"The instant we fit the two halves together we knew we weren't dealing with an apelike *Australopithecus*," said Dr. Kimbel, who was at the site at the time of the discovery.

A species like *Australopithecus afarensis*, which lived from 3.9 million years ago to at least 3 million, had a long, narrow palate and projecting face, giving its skull an apelike visage. But the Hadar jaw is broader, with a parabolic dental arch. Other characteristics suggested that the individual had a short, flat nose, more like *Homo* than *Australopithecus*, and did not have a projecting, apelike face.

With no more to go on, Dr. Kimbel said in an interview, it was impossible to say if the jaw belonged to either of the two previously known early *Homo* species in East Africa, generally classified as *Homo habilis* and *Homo rudolfensis*, or the later *Homo erectus*. The evolutionary path from *Homo erectus* to *Homo sapiens* is a subject of much debate, but anatomically modern *Homo sapiens sapiens* is thought to have arisen from 200,000 to 100,000 years ago.

Dr. Kimbel said that if anything, the jaw bore more resemblance to *Homo habilis*. "That is based primarily on the fact that *habilis* is likewise more primitive than any other *Homo*," he explained.

Dr. Eric Delson, a paleontologist at the American Museum of Natural History and the City University of New York, said, "It's conceivable that this jaw could be something different, neither *habilis* nor *rudolfensis*."

This prospect is especially intriguing. Since paleontologists have reservations about *H. habilis* or *H. rudolfensis* as species on the direct ancestral line to modern humans, Dr. Delson said, it could be "possibly extremely important" if the jaw proved to be a distinct species that might be on the mainline of human evolution.

Other investigations at Hadar have provided more evidence of drastic environmental change in this period. Abundant fossils of antelopes recovered at the site indicate that the region was fairly open and grassy, with some water not far away. In the time of *A. afarensis*, before 3 million years ago, Hadar was a wetter, more densely wooded area teeming with impalas and other woodland mammals.

Some paleontologists, notably Dr. Elisabeth Vrba of Yale, suspect that the origin of the *Homo* lineage could have been influenced by the onset of a colder global climate, beginning about 2.7 million years ago. At about that time, it is thought that *A. afarensis*, the Lucy species, split into at least two lineages, *A. africanus* and *A. aethiopicus*, and a third group may have appeared as well—*Homo*.

"The Hadar fossil," Dr. Johanson said, "helps plug a gap in the evidence for the early evolution of our own lineage and perhaps will help us begin to forge links back in time to *A. afarensis*."

Other paleontologists in the last two years have begun filling in another crucial gap in the hominid fossil record. This is the period after the hominids split from the apes, about 7 million to 5 million years ago, and before the first known evidence for *A. afarensis*, about 3.9 million years ago.

Last year Dr. Meave Leakey of the Kenya National Museum in Nairobi and Dr. Alan Walker of Pennsylvania State University uncovered fossils in Kenya of a 4.1-million-year-old species, designated *A. anamensis*. And Dr. Tim D. White of the University of California at Berkeley identified an even more apelike hominid, the 4.4-million-year-old *Ardipithecus ramidus*, from fossils found in Ethiopia. Both show early evidence for the transition to upright walking.

Editor's note: Since this article appeared, new fossil discoveries have emerged. This is not unexpected, as the field of paleoanthropology itself continues to evolve in the wake of new finds. John Noble Wilford reports in this article that the number of hominid species has grown considerably over the years, yet there is always room for the discovery of one more "missing link." Don Johanson's fossil finds of the genus *Homo* at Hadar extended our knowledge of hominid evolution back several hundreds of thousands of years, "forging links back in time to *A. afarensis*." The newest member of the early hominid group also contributes to this goal. Excavated in 1997 near the village of Bouri, Middle Awash, Ethiopia, the fossil—a fragmentary skull—consists of the upper jaw, rather large dentition, and the brow ridge part of the frontal bone. A number of characters of the skull appear to be more advanced than those of the earlier *afarensis*, yet certain expectations concerning brain size and the dentition for a missing link at this time period were exactly met. Thus, the name appropriately bestowed on the find, *Australopithecus garhi*, means "surprise" in the language of the local Afar people. Perhaps even more surprising was the accumulation of worked bone and stone found in association with the hominid bones. Researcher team leaders Berhane Asfaw and Tim White found fossil bones of antelope and other species that had cut marks, the legacy of stone tool butchering activities, along with stone tools perhaps responsible for making those marks. While one should always err on the side of caution in this business, it is quite possible that the stone tool maker previously unknown from the nearby archeological site of Gona has now been exposed.

Postscript: In 1993 and again in 1996 I accompanied archeologist J. Desmond Clark and geologist Jean de Heinzelin (now deceased) to Bouri for archeological reconnaissance in the arid hills and wadis of this isolated region. We must have walked by the exact area where this fossil lay buried just under the surface on these eroding deposits hundreds of times with never a clue as to what we were missing. The rains that came to Bouri after we left in 1996 were enough to expose the fossils and tools for the 1997 team to find. Such is the luck in paleoanthropological field work.

THE NEW YORK TIMES

Friday, December 13, 1996

Three Human Species Coexisted Eons Ago, New Data Suggest

By JOHN NOBLE WILFORD

Scientists have found stunning new data showing that a third human species apparently coexisted on earth with two others as recently as 30,000 years ago.

In research that could redraw the human family tree and is certain to be controversial, the scientists re-examined two major fossil sites along the Solo River in Java and found that an early human relative, *Homo erectus*, appeared to have lived there until about 27,000 to 53,000 years ago.

Writing in today's issue of the journal *Science*, the scientists said the new dates were "surprisingly young and, if proven correct, imply that *H. erectus* persisted much longer in Southeast Asia than elsewhere in the world."

Confirmation of the new dates would mean that at least in Java, this archaic species, which evolved 1.8 million years ago, survived some 250,000 years after it was thought to have become extinct. This surviving population of *H. erectus* in Indonesia would have been alive at the same time as anatomically modern humans—*Homo sapiens*—and also Neanderthals, whose exact place in human evolution is a subject of endless debate.

The Neanderthals, who lived in Europe and western Asia for some 300,000 years, appear to have made their last stand 30,000 years ago in southern Spain. By then, modern *H. sapiens*, who are widely thought to have evolved in Africa 200,000 to 100,000 years ago, had spread all over Africa and Eurasia, as far as Australia. It is not known how much contact the three species had, or if they could interbreed.

In any case, specialists in human evolution noted, the new findings suggest that the present phenomenon of a solitary human species on earth may be more the exception than the rule. Until about a couple of decades ago, scientists conceived of the human lineage as a neat progression of one species to the next and generally thought it impossible that two species could have overlapped in place or time.

Another implication of the more recent date for *H. erectus* is to undercut a pillar of the multiregional theory for the origin of modern *H. sapiens*.

As the most advanced known representatives of *H. erectus*, the Java fossils have appeared to be a clear intermediate step in the evolution of *H. erectus* in Southeast Asia to the first Australians, who were modern *H. sapiens*. This has lent support to the idea that modern humans emerged gradually out of *H. erectus* in many parts of the world. The alternative and more favored out-of-Africa theory holds that modern humans evolved in Africa less than 200,000 years ago and displaced *H. erectus* as they migrated to the ends of the earth.

The team of scientists, led by Dr. Carl C. Swisher of the Berkeley Geochronology Center in California, concluded that it was "no longer chronologically plausible" to argue that the Java *H. erectus* evolved into Asian *H. sapiens*. From earlier fossil evidence, Australian *H. sapiens* are at least 30,000 years old, and could be much older, judging by rock art.

"The multiregionalists will have to do some fast talking to explain this," said Dr. Philip Rightmire, a paleoanthropologist at the State University of New York at Binghamton. "It's quite a blow for them to absorb. But neither side has won the day yet in this theoretical battle."

Dr. Milford Wolpoff, a paleoanthropologist at the University of Michigan who is an outspoken leader of the multiregional theorists, questioned both the accuracy of the dates and the identification of the skulls at the Java sites, contending that they were *H. sapiens* and not *H. erectus*. Dr. Wolpoff said these questions should have been answered more convincingly before the team published its report.

As one who has studied the skulls at Ngandong, one of the two sites, and compared them with early Australian *H. sapiens*, Dr. Wolpoff said the idea of an ancestral "link between them is incontrovertible."

In an accompanying article in *Science*, Dr. Alan Thorne of the Australian National University in Canberra, one of Dr. Wolpoff's allies, said, "There is a great long list of characters that are the same in the Solo skulls and the earliest known human people from Australia."

Even if the Java fossils are indeed relatively young, Dr. Thorne added, they look so much like the Australian fossils that the two species may have shared a recent ancestor.

Both Dr. Rightmire, an authority on *H. erectus*, and Dr. Susan C. Anton, a paleoanthropologist at the University of Florida who was a member of Dr. Swisher's team, said they were satisfied that the Java specimens were *H. erectus*, though the skulls did show signs of their having evolved a somewhat larger brain than earlier members of the species. That *H. erectus* and *H. sapiens* now appear to have overlapped, Dr. Anton said, "raises the possibility of gene flow between the two lines."

The Java fossils were discovered in the 1930s by Dutch geologists. Over the years, various efforts to date the specimens have yielded ages of as high as 300,000 and 250,000 years and, recently, as low as 100,000 years.

The most reliable means of dating such ancient material is to determine the age of volcanic ash in the sediments, but none is associated with the Solo specimens. Similarly, a number of other techniques were not suitable, and the skulls themselves could not be dated because they would have been damaged.

Dr. Swisher explained in an interview that he had dug a test trench at the Ngandong site, on a terrace at the bend in the Solo River. He noted that the layer of sediment where the skulls had been found also contained teeth of water buffalo. The teeth were analyzed through two techniques for measuring the radioactive decay of uranium that the teeth had absorbed from the soil. This indicated how long the teeth had been buried.

To assure themselves that they were sampling the same sediment layer where the *H. erectus* skulls had been excavated, the scientists said, they compared and dated similar water buffalo teeth collected by the Dutch geologists at the time of the original discoveries. The specimens are kept at Gadjah Mada University in Yogyakarta, Indonesia. The dating analysis was conducted at McMaster University in Hamilton, Ontario.

Some scientists said they were still concerned that erosion and river currents could have mixed up older *H. erectus* skulls with younger water buffalo teeth, but Dr. Swisher said this was unlikely to have occurred in the same way for 12 different skulls at two widely separated sites.

If the dates are right, as Dr. Swisher's team noted at the conclusion of its report, "the temporal and spatial overlap between *H. erectus* and *H. sapiens* in Southeast Asia is reminiscent of the overlap of Neanderthals (*H. neanderthalensis*) and anatomically modern humans in Europe."

SCIENCE

July 10, 1998

Geological Analysis Damps
Ancient Chinese Fires

By BERNICE WEUTHRICH

Studies of sediments at Zhoukoudian, China—long considered the site of the first use of fire—suggests that any flames there were not kindled by human hands.

When and where did our human ancestors stop running from fire and start guarding and preserving it as a vital tool for survival? For the last half-century, nearly every archaeology textbook has offered a simple answer to that question: 500,000 years ago, in Zhoukoudian, China, where Peking man—*Homo erectus*—huddled around a hearth tending kindling and roasting deer.

But that answer is now up for revision, according to a reanalysis of the Zhoukoudian site.... "In a sense, we spoil the story," says ... structural biologist Steve Weiner of the Weizmann Institute for Science in Rehovot, Israel. Applying a battery of techniques, Weiner and his colleagues did confirm that there are some burnt bones at the site about 30 miles southwest of Beijing, but those might have been burned naturally. And they found no evidence of controlled use of fires: no hearths, no ashes, and none of the unique chemical signatures expected from fires.

The signs of fires at Zhoukoudian are now no clearer than at dozens of older sites around the world. "The bones are burnt, but we don't have the smoking gun: the fireplaces which people assumed to have been there," says ... geoarchaeologist Paul Goldberg of Boston University. That means there's no strong evidence of fire use until about 300,000 years ago and none definitively associated with *H. erectus*, the hominid that began to spread through

Asia and into cold northern latitudes starting about 1.8 million years ago. Researchers must now consider that this colonization may have happened without fire. "We now have to reconsider *H. erectus,* their migrations, and their capability," says Huang Weiwen, and archaeologist of Vertebrate Paleontology and Paleoanthropology (IVPP) in Beijing, who has worked extensively at Zhoukoudian.

The site was first excavated in the 1920s and '30s, when researchers found hominid fossils, stone tools, burnt bones, and what they described as ancient hearths preserved as layers of ash up to several meters thick. It all seemed to add up to solid evidence of human control of fire; some researchers even concluded that the thick ash layers represented continuous occupation over thousands of years.

The new study is the "first really systematic investigation since the early excavations," notes anthropologist Rick Potts at the National Museum of Natural History in Washington, D.C. In 1996 and 1997, Weiner's team revisited the site, a sheer cliff cut into the hillside, perching on a 10-story-high scaffolding for their analysis. They focused on layers 10 and 4, previously noted for putative king-sized hearths. They cleaned the exposure, studied the sediments microscopically, and used infrared spectrometry onsite to analyze the chemical constituents of sediments and fossil bone. In the lab, they confirmed that a small number of bones were burned. But the sediments contained no ash or siliceous aggregates, soil-derived minerals that are cemented together in trees and stay intact after burning—and should be present at the site of almost any wood fires. The thick layers aren't ash at all, but accumulations of organic material, much of it laid down under water, says Weiner.

The team did find stone tools closely associated with burnt mammal bones. And more of these bones came from large animals than small, a proportion considered consistent with human activity, because people are more likely to roast horse than mice for dinner. But although this clearly indicates the presence of fire somewhere nearby, it doesn't convince most researchers that humans rather than nature sparked the flames. That's part of the reason why even older purported evidence of fire—up to 1.8 million years old— from sites in Africa and Asia has been considered "dubious," says paleoanthropologist Philip Rightmire at the State University of New York, Binghamton. "The whole thing is [now] ambiguous, and that's the normal situation," adds anthropologist Lewis Binford of Southern Methodist University in Dallas, who visited Zhoukoudian briefly in the 1980s and first challenged the interpretation of hearths.

The paper also raises questions about whether humans actually lived at the site, because the researchers describe it not as a traditional cave but as the enlargement of a vertical fault, open to the sky. "This is an important reinterpretation," says Potts. "It means that, who knows, maybe it wasn't a home." Anthropologist Alison Brooks at George Washington University in Washington, D.C., who has also worked at the site, goes further: "It wouldn't have been a shelter, it would have been a trap." Taken together, the evidence "brings Zhoukoudian a good deal more in line with sites from around the world, with a low fingerprint of human activity," says anthropologist Chris Stringer of the Natural History Museum in London.

The first strong evidence of purposeful use of fire is now associated with much younger humans. "This puts it forward at least to *H. heidelbergensis* and may push it forward to Neandertal," says Brooks. A leading candidate may be Vértesszöllös, Hungary, an *H. heidelbergensis* site between 400,000 and 200,000 years old, where burned bone is arranged in a radial pattern as if around a campfire. "That spatial evidence is missing for Zhoukoudian," says Potts.

...

Still, some scientists advise against drawing sweeping conclusions from this single study. "The researchers were limited by the area they sampled," far from the center of the cave, points out Huang. "Therefore, it is not an ideal place to detect the evidence of controlled fire use," adds Gao Xing, an archaeologist formerly with the IVPP and now at the University of Arizona, Tucson.

Nonetheless, ambiguity at Zhoukoudian raises questions about whether *H. erectus* anywhere used fire, Stringer says. Yet the species somehow survived in Zhoukoudian's temperate climate and colonized lands even farther north. The absence of fire suggests that *H. erectus* was much less advanced, argues Brooks. But other recent discoveries have suggested that the species was a sophisticated toolmaker, points out Huang, and perhaps even traveled by boat (*Science*, 13 March, p. 1635). For now, the dampened flame at Zhoukoudian has thrown these ancient humans into deeper shadow. "This work is another new beginning, but it is not enough to answer all the questions we are curious to know," says Huang.

SCIENCE

March 13, 1998

Ancient Island Tools Suggest
Homo Erectus Was a Seafarer

By Ann Gibbons

In 1968, a Dutch missionary living on the Indonesian island of Flores found stone tools alongside the bones of an extinct type of elephant called a *Stegodon*, known to have lived at least 750,000 years ago. If the tools were as old as the *Stegodon*, this was a spectacular discovery, for Flores lies beyond a deep-water strait that separates most Asian and Australian faunas. The tools meant that the only human species then living in Southeast Asia, *Homo erectus*, must have been able to cross this biological barrier, called Wallace's line.

But when the missionary, Theodor Verhoeven, reported his findings in the journal *Anthropos*, his claim was roundly dismissed. Although trained in classical archaeology, Verhoeven was an amateur, so researcher's discounted his field work. And the accepted idea was that deep waters blocked human exploration until about 50,000 years ago. Although *H. erectus* was known from just 600 kilometers away on Java, most researchers were convinced that this early human lacked the social and linguistic skills needed to cross Wallace's line by piloting a raft over deep, fast-moving waters. Even after Dutch and Indonesian paleontologists backed Verhoeven's findings with new excavations and paleomagnetic dating in 1994, the claim was still considered dubious.

... [Now an] international team presents new dates for stone tools from Flores, based on a different and more reliable technique called fission-track dating, that confirm *H. erectus*'s presence there 800,000 years ago. The authors propose that the early humans who left behind these simple flakes and cobbles were "capable of repeated water crossings using watercraft" and may even have had language, needed to cooperate to build rafts. The "cognitive capabilities of *H. erectus* may be due for reappraisal," says archaeologist Mike Morwood of the University of New England in Armidale, Australia, lead author of the paper.

Most researchers accept the new dates for the artifacts, but they are sharply divided over what the findings reveal about the toolmaker. A few questions linger about whether the artifacts are really tools—and no *H. erectus* bones have been found on Flores to dispel these questions. Some researchers add that *H. erectus* might have accidentally drifted over to Flores on a raft or even walked on some previously unknown land bridge, says Colin Groves of Australian National University (ANU) in Canberra: "The Flores data do not seem convincing that *H. erectus* made boats." Nonetheless, he agrees with others that the tools "are quite remarkable evidence of the distributional extent and environmental flexibility of our perhaps underestimated cousin, *H. erectus.*"

H. erectus in Asia has long been eclipsed by its relatives in Africa, where the species is thought to have arisen more than 1.8 million years ago. In the first known exodus of human beings from Africa, *H. erectus* then spread around the globe, settling in China and Java perhaps as early as 1.8 million years ago.... But although these early humans spread thousands of kilometers over land and across shallow straits, they seemed to have been incapable of deep-water crossings. In technical, social, and organizational skills—not to mention language—*H. erectus* was thought to lag far behind humans.

H. erectus's limitations seemed especially severe in Asia. Starting 1.5 million years ago, the Africans made better tools—two-sided stone hand axes—while the Asian members of the species either left almost no tools, as in Java, or only simple cobblestone choppers and flakes. "This group of Eastern hominids has always been regarded as impoverished in technological or cultural capabilities, as compared to their contemporaries in Africa," says Philip Rightmire, a paleoanthropologist at the State University of New York, Binghamton.

For the past 4 years, however, Dutch and Indonesian paleontologists have been coming up with support for Verhoeven's 1968 claim—and for a more flattering picture of Asian *H. erectus.* A Dutch and Indonesian group led by Paul Sondaar of the Natural History Museum in Rotterdam, the Netherlands, applied paleomagnetic dating, which is based on well-known reversals in Earth's magnetic field recorded in volcanic rock, to a rock layer just below 14 stone artifacts they had found in volcanic ash beds at a site called Mata Menge. The dates, about 750,000 years old, nicely matched Verhoeven's. But the results, published in 1994 and 1997 in French and Australian journals, were considered suspect. That was partly because of the lack of human bones and the uncertainties of this type of dating at the site....

Now new dating of ash layers from Mata dispel the notion that *H. erectus* in general, and Eastern *H. erectus* in particular, were relatively slow to react to challenges posed by the environment," because they not only navigated deep-water straits but adapted to life on an island, where the environment is thought to have been far different from the forest habitat of the mainland.

The new findings also fit well with other work showing that Asian *H. erectus* has been underrated. Controversial new dates from sites in Java suggest that *H. erectus* persisted there from as early as 1.8 million years ago until as recently as 30,000 years ago, implying that they were able to adapt to varied terrain and climate. Other new studies suggest that *H. erectus* left behind sophisticated hand axes in southern China. For those who have worked on Flores and long believed in *H. erectus*'s presence there, the new results are vindication....

THE NEW YORK TIMES

Friday, May 30, 1997

Fossils Called Limb
in Human Family Tree

By John Noble Wilford

Spanish paleontologists say 800,000-year-old fossils they found in a limestone cave represent an entirely new species of human ancestor and could be the last common ancestor of modern humans and their extinct cousins, the Neanderthals.

Other scientists are not so sure. They agree that the fossils, whatever their species, are remains of the earliest known Europeans. As such, the fossils are critical to an understanding of how Europe was first settled by hominids, the family of all human species, alive and extinct. But scientists expressed serious reservations about assigning the Spanish fossils to a separate limb on the family tree.

A Spanish team of paleontologists, led by Dr. Jose M. Bermudez de Castro of the National Museum of Natural Sciences and Dr. Juan Luis Arsuaga of the Complutense University, both in Madrid, based their case for a new hominid species on the bones of a boy with a remarkably modern face. The partial remains of the boy, about 10 or 11 years old, and five other individuals were discovered two years ago at the Gran Dolina cave in the Atapuerca hills near Burgos, Spain.

Everything about the boy's cranium, lower jaw and teeth, the researchers could see, was primitive. But between the brow and the jaw, the sunken cheeks, projecting nose and other traits suggested "a completely modern pattern of midfacial topography," the paleontologists wrote in a report being published today in the journal *Science*.

72

This combination of modern and primitive characteristics seems to set the Atapuerca boy apart from any previously recognized species, the researchers said. No hominids had been known to have developed such a modern face earlier than 200,000 years ago. And the primitive aspects do not seem to be like those of *Homo heidelbergensis*, the Heidelberg Man of 500,000 years ago, which had been the earliest known hominid in Western Europe.

Accordingly, the paleontologists decided the fossils belonged to a separate species and proposed that it be named *Homo antecessor*, meaning "one who goes before."

As if proposing a new hominid species was not enough to provoke impassioned debate, the Spanish team invited further controversy by identifying the 800,000-year-old species, not *Homo heidelbergensis* or the even earlier *Homo erectus*, as the probable common ancestor of Neanderthals and modern humans, *Homo sapiens*. The robust, heavy-browed Neanderthals appeared in Europe about 200,000 years ago and vanished about 28,000 years ago. Many scientists think *Homo sapiens* evolved in Africa 200,000 to 100,000 years ago and arrived in Europe about 40,000 years ago.

The journal quoted Dr. Antonio Rosas, another paleontologist from the Madrid museum and member of the team, as saying the boy's facial traits are "exactly the morphology we would imagine in the common ancestor of modern humans and Neanderthals."

One way to account for *Homo antecessor*'s role as ancestor to both Neanderthals and modern humans, the Spanish researchers said, is to postulate the origin of the new species in Africa, though no similar fossils have been found there. Some members of *Homo antecessor* in Africa gave rise eventually to *Homo sapiens*, according to the hypothesis, while others migrated to Europe, possibly about a million years ago. The European branch then evolved into *Homo heidelbergensis*, which in turn led to Neanderthals.

But many paleontologists are not yet prepared to accept *Homo antecessor* as a distinct species.

"I'm reluctant to endorse this new species," said Dr. Philip Rightmire, a paleoanthropologist at the State University of New York at Binghamton. "I wonder if the facial characteristics of one juvenile are really diagnostic. It's tricky to compare children to adults and on that basis establish a new species."

Dr. Fred H. Smith, a paleoanthropologist at Northern Illinois University in DeKalb who specializes in European hominids, said the Gran Dolina fossils were "interesting and important" but "insufficient evidence for a new species."

Dr. Smith said the fossils would probably turn out to be either an early *Homo heidelbergensis* or late *Homo erectus*. Dr. Rightmire said he saw no reason yet to reconsider his idea that *Homo heidelbergensis* was the last common ancestor of Neanderthals and modern humans.

But Dr. Rosas said the few pieces of facial bones from the adults collected in the cave, a discovery announced last in 1995, also showed some of the same modern-looking characteristics found in the boy's face. He insisted that the team had enough evidence to support the designation of a new species, while acknowledging that "people are probably going to need some time to accommodate this proposal."

4

CULTURAL ORIGINS, LANGUAGE, AND COGNITIVE ABILITIES

Exactly what and how much can we understand about ourselves by studying the behavior of the nonhuman primates? Is it true, as Senator Edward Kennedy and Representative John Dingell wrote, that "primate research is a preposterous basis for discussing the crime and violence that plagues our country today"? But how preposterous is this notion? Studies of the behavior of the nonhuman primates in the wild stretch back about forty years; further, if you include the first work of Japanese primatologists who studied homeland macaque monkeys, and further still with the work on gibbons and howler monkeys by Clarence Ray Carpenter in the late 1930s and early 1940s. However, field work became popular as an occupation after the pioneering work on African baboons by Sherwood Washburn (UC Berkeley) and Irven DeVore (Harvard), beginning in the late 1950s, and became popular as an armchair pastime for countless readers and television viewers alike after Jane Goodall began her work on the chimpanzees at the Gombe Stream Reserve in Tanzania. Female powerhouses such as Flo and her daughter Fifi, the antics of her son Flint, the power struggles of Wilkie and Getty, and the murderous adventures of Pom and her mother are all stories well known to the generation of human contemporaries. Not only have we been amused, but also we have related in some form or fashion to these stories about our quadrupedal cousins. The awareness that there is something similar in the behaviors of human and nonhuman primates makes the study of primate behavior all the more intriguing for scientist and layman alike. Intrigue sparks curiosity. Curiosity sparks the formulation of specific questions and ideas about how to answer them. The fossil evidence can tell us a few things about the evolution of human behavior, but our models of understanding nearly always use to some degree behavior research based on these close relatives. The articles in this chapter look at some of the recent research discoveries in the field of primate social behavior and comment on their significance in our understanding of our own behavior.

Early field studies focused on the behavior of the adult male members of the troop. Male dominance and aggression were emphasized in these early reports; the observations of the behavior of females almost invariably stressed reproductive activities and child rearing. The human story of man the hunter and provider and woman the bearer of children was replayed, only changing the characters from human to nonhuman primate. In recent years our understanding of the role of the female in the social organization of the troop has changed almost completely. We know now that most primate troops are organized around a stable group of female matrilines and that female dominance hierarchies are stable and those of the males are not. Unbeknownst to early field scientists, almost all of the males born into one social group migrate to others sometime during their life span and male social rank can change dramatically over time. Natalie Angier of the *New York Times*, in her article "Bonobo Society: Amicable, Amorous, and Run by Females," reports on the social organization of the bonobo chimpanzee that illustrates these new findings.

How do female primates make their considerable influence felt, and what effect do high-ranking females have on other members of the troop? In her article "In Society of Female Chimps, Subtle Signs of Vital Status," Natalie Angier describes research from Jane Goodall's study site at the Gombe Stream Reserve showing that while dominant female influence may be subtle, it has significant effect on the reproductive success of those afforded lesser rank.

Through their available modes of communication, nonhuman primates were thought to be capable only of transmitting simple emotional condition or state. But vocal playback experiments that recorded primate vocalizations showed that these animals had the ability to communicate much more. Age, gender, kinship affiliation, and rank are all messages that the nonhuman primates can send. Nonvocal communication can also have subtle meaning, as the *New York Times* article "Road Maps of Apes" reports.

The search for evolutionary explanations of human behavior patterns certainly reached a milestone with the publication of Darwin's *Expression of the Emotions in Man and Animals* (1872). Humans can be nice (sometimes) and altruistic (though mostly toward their kin). David Papineau, a professor of philosophy at King's College, London, and the editor of *The Philosophy of Science*, gives us his thoughts on the matter in his article "You Scratch My Back, I'll Scratch Yours," in which he reviews Matt Ridley's *The Origin of Virtue* and Frans de Waal's *The Forgotten Ape*. He concludes that, while biology does influence our behavior, it does not rule it, and that traits that humans have inherited that aren't so nice can be subsumed by cultural practices that are. In the brief letter "Evolution and Morality," which follows Papineau's review, anthropologist Lionel Tiger adds his ideas.

David Berreby carries the argument further in his commentary about the humaneness of animals, entitled "Are Apes Naughty by Nature?" That apes and humans have been separated in time from their common ancestor for about 5 million years tends to obscure relationships and to underestimate animal cognitive abilities. Berreby presents the arguments of primatologist Frans de Waal, who believes that overestimating these abilities is probably a "healthy reaction" to the critics.

Nonhuman primates, like humans, aren't always nice. Mark Ridley's article "Going Ape" and Christopher Lehmann-Haupt's article "How Did Man Get So Bad? Looking to the Apes," both of which review Richard Wrangham and Dale Peterson's book *Demonic Males*, show how not-so-nice some of the nonhuman primates can really be. In this turn of the coin, murder and mayhem are the themes presented. When we return to the notion of the preposterousness of using primate behavior studies to show us anything that might be useful in understanding human violence, we find the argument fractured.

Perhaps the best known of the current researchers in the field of primate communication and human language is Emily Sue Savage-Rumbaugh of Georgia State University. Claudia Dreifus of the *New York Times*—in her article "A Conversation with Emily Sue Savage-Rumbaugh: She Talks to Apes and, According to Her, They Talk Back"—reports an interview with Savage-Rumbaugh in which she discusses what apes are capable of in the language domain. Apes can't speak, but through the use of sight, sounds, signs, and symbols they can convey specific meanings.

If a continuum really exists in the evolution of human language from those communication skills possessed by the apes, then can we learn anything further about this issue by studying the human fossil record? What imprint, if any, do the fossils have that could tell us whether or not they could speak? In two articles—"Ancestral Humans Could Speak, Anthropologists' Finding Suggests" and "Look Who's Talking; Don't Bother Listening"—John Wilford Noble of the *New York Times* describes human fossils of the genus *Homo* from over 400,000 years ago whose preserved bony canals of the nerves that innervate the muscles of the tongue are the same as those found in modern humans. Did the sounds that these hominids made resemble modern human sounds? It's still difficult to tell.

The bottom line in speech abilities involves the brain. We have known about speech "centers" in the brain from research that dates back to the middle 1800s. Supposed asymmetries in the brain in the area of the planum temporale were also thought to be significant in human's ability to speak. In her article "Brain of Chimpanzee Sheds Light on Mystery of Language," Sandra Blakeslee reports on research that supports a new notion that language isn't so much related to brain centers and areas as it is to the development of novel connections that allow language function to be widely distributed throughout the whole brain.

In Philip Lieberman's new book *Eve Spoke*, the Eve that is referred to is not the Eve of Old Testament fame. Rather, this Eve's renown comes from studies of mitochondrial DNA, research that supports the widely held view that modern humans emerged in Africa some 150,000 years ago and, subsequently, migrated from there to other parts of the Old World. Lieberman is well known in the field of vocal tract reconstructions of fossil hominids, especially those of the Neanderthals. Lieberman's work and interpretations of the evidence for early human speech that is provided by others are reviewed in Derek Bickerton's article "Madam, I'm Adam." (Bickerton himself has contributed significantly to untangling the question of language origins. His most recent books are *Language and Species* and *Language and Human Behavior*.) In "Origin of Speech," a brief response to Bickerton's review, Lieberman gives us his views on the issues that Bickerton raises.

However human speech arose and developed, it has the capacity to stir our emotions as only few nonhuman primate sounds can do. Listening to some people speak has the power to make us hate or love, fall asleep, or stay perched on the edge of our seats. Verlyn Klinkenborg, in "The Material Basis of the Human Voice," relates to us the emotional power of human language that can be signaled even if we do not understand the meaning of a single word that, in this case, is sung.

THE NEW YORK TIMES

Tuesday, April 22, 1997

Bonobo Society:
Amicable, Amorous,
and Run by Females

BY NATALIE ANGIER

Nature's raucous bestiary rarely serves up good role models for human behavior, unless you happen to work on the trading floor of the New York
Stock Exchange. But there is one creature that stands out from the chest-
thumping masses as an example of amicability, sensitivity and, well, humaneness: a little-known ape called the bonobo, or, less accurately, the
pygmy chimpanzee.

Before bonobos can be fully appreciated, however, two human preju-
dices must be overcome. The first is, fellows, the female bonobo is the dominant sex, though the dominance is so mild and unobnoxious that some
researchers view bonobo society as a matter of "co-dominance," or equality
between the sexes. Fancy that.

The second hurdle is human squeamishness about what in the 80s were
called P.D.A.s, or public displays of affection, in this case very graphic ones.
Bonobos lubricate the gears of social harmony with sex, in all possible per-
mutations and combinations: males with females, males with males, females
with females, and even infants with adults. The sexual acts include inter-
course, genital-to-genital rubbing, oral sex, mutual masturbation and even a
practice that people once thought they had a patent on: French kissing.

Bonobos use sex to appease, to bond, to make up after a fight, to ease
tensions, to cement alliances. Humans generally wait until after a nice meal
to make love; bonobos do it beforehand, to alleviate the stress and competi-
tiveness often seen among animals when they encounter a source of food.

Lest this all sound like a nonstop Caligulean orgy, Frans de Waal, a primatologist at Emory University in Atlanta who is the author of *Bonobo: The Forgotten Ape*, emphasizes otherwise. "Sex is there, it's pervasive, it's critical, and bonobo society would collapse without it," he said in an interview. "But it's not what people think it is. It's not driven by orgasm or seeking release. Nor is it often reproductively driven. Sex for a bonobo is casual, it's quick and once you're used to watching it, it begins to look like any other social interaction." The new book, with photographs by Frans Lanting, will be published in May by the University of California Press.

In *Bonobo*, Dr. de Waal draws upon his own research as well as that of many other primatologists to sketch a portrait of a species much less familiar to most people than are the other great apes—the gorilla, the orangutan and the so-called common chimpanzee. The bonobo, found in the dense equatorial rain forests of Zaire, was not officially discovered until 1929, long after the other apes had been described in the scientific literature.

Even today there are only about 100 in zoos around the country, compared with the many thousands of chimpanzees in captivity. Bonobos are closely related to chimpanzees, but they have a more graceful and slender build, with smaller heads, slimmer necks, longer legs and less burly upper torsos. When standing or walking upright, bonobos have straighter backs than do the chimpanzees, and so assume a more humanlike posture.

Far more dramatic than their physical differences are their behavioral distinctions. Bonobos are much less aggressive and hot-tempered than are chimpanzees, and are not nearly as prone to physical violence. They are less obsessed with power and status than are their chimpanzee cousins, and more consumed with Eros.

As Dr. de Waal puts it in his book, "The chimpanzee resolves sexual issues with power; the bonobo resolves power issues with sex." Or more coyly, chimpanzees are from Mars, bonobos are from Venus.

All of which has relevance for understanding the roots of human nature. Dr. de Waal seeks to correct the image of humanity's ancestors as invariably chimpanzee-like, driven by aggression, hierarchical machinations, hunting, warfare and male dominance. He points out that bonobos are as genetically close to humans as are chimpanzees, and that both are astonishingly similar to mankind, sharing at least 98 percent of humans' DNA. "The take-home message is, there's more flexibility in our lineage than we thought," Dr. de Waal said. "Bonobos are just as close to us as are chimpanzees, so we can't push them aside."

Indeed, humans appear to possess at least some bonobo-like characteristics, particularly the extracurricular use of sex beyond that needed for reproduction, and perhaps a more robust capacity for cooperation than some die-hard social Darwinists might care to admit.

One unusual aspect of bonobo society is the ability of females to form strong alliances with other unrelated females. In most primates, the males leave their birthplaces on reaching maturity as a means of avoiding incest, and so the females that form the social core are knit together by kinship. Among bonobos, females disperse at adolescence, and have to insinuate themselves into a group of strangers. They make friends with sexual overtures, and are particularly solicitous of the resident females.

The constructed sisterhood appears to give females a slight edge over resident males, who, though they may be related to one another, do not tend to act as an organized alliance. For example, the females usually have priority when it comes to eating, and they will stick up for one another should the bigger and more muscular male try to act aggressively. Female alliances may have arisen to counter the threat of infanticide by males, which is quite common in other species, including the chimpanzee, but has never been observed among bonobos.

Dr. de Waal said that many men grow indignant when they learn of the bonobo's social structure. "After one of my talks, a famous German professor jumped up and said, 'What is wrong with these males?'" he recalled. Yet Dr. de Waal said the bonobo males might not have reason to rebel. "They seem to be in a perfectly good situation," he said. "The females have sex with them all the time, and they don't have to fight over it so much among themselves. I'm not sure they've lost anything, except for their dominance."

THE NEW YORK TIMES

Tuesday, August 12, 1997

In Society of Female Chimps, Subtle Signs of Vital Status

By Natalie Angier

Much to the surprise of primatologists, a dominant female chimpanzee turns out to be a lot like Alan Greenspan, the all-mighty czar of the Federal Reserve. He clears his throat, and stock markets tumble. She twitches an ear, and her underlings tremble. He controls the economy without so much as passing a law. She affects her group's fecundity without so much as raising a paw. Both man and ape offer proof that you don't have to speak much, you don't even have to carry a big stick, and still you can rule the world.

Scientists have discovered that female chimpanzees, long believed to have little or no interest in pulling rank on each other, in fact form subtle social hierarchies that profoundly influence the fate and fertility of every female in the group.

Working in the Gombe National Park of Tanzania with Jane Goodall, Anne Pusey and Jennifer Williams of the University of Minnesota have determined that female chimpanzees differ far more in their individual ability to bear and rear offspring than anybody had suspected, and that one of the biggest factors influencing a female's reproductive prowess is her social status. The babies of a high-ranking female are much likelier to survive to independence than are the offspring of a subordinate chimpanzee, and the daughters of a dominant mother reach sexual maturity four years earlier than those of a low-ranking female, a spectacular advantage that can transform a dominant family into a dynastic one.

But for all the discrepancies in prospects that are tied to social status, female chimpanzees appear indifferent to displays of power. They do not brandish fallen branches or kick over oil drums, as a male will to flaunt his status. They rarely fight with each other, and when they do, it is hard to tell who won. They are not big socializers, spending most of their time alone in the forest with their dependent young. Should a female encounter a male from her group, she will make the appropriate noises of subordination, giving off a little hnn-hnn-hnn sound called a pant-grunt, as a low-ranking male will in the presence of a dominant male. But when two females meet, they often ignore each other.

"The big surprise here is that dominance rank is so subtle as to be nonexistent, yet it has huge impact on reproductive success," said Ms. Williams, who is working on her doctoral dissertation. The findings of the new study appear in [an] issue of the journal *Science*.

"People had emphasized the importance of rank among male chimpanzees, because it was so easy to see," said Dr. Craig Packer of the University of Minnesota, who did not contribute to the chimpanzee study but is familiar with it. "The females looked like the nebbishes of the woods," he said.

When Dr. Pusey and her colleagues began analyzing chimpanzee behavioral patterns more carefully, they found that beneath the females' apparently distracted exteriors skulked true political animals. Using data from the renowned Gombe chimpanzee field study that Dr. Goodall began in 1960, the scientists assessed dominance by looking at all pant-grunts exchanged in a group of 10 females from 1970 through 1992. They found that while pant-grunting is not an inevitable feature of female greeting, when it did occur between a given pair, it was always in the same direction: If female A pant-grunted to female B one day, A would pant-grunt to B the following year. By considering this reliable if inconspicuous vocalization, the researchers found that the females aligned themselves into a fairly stable hierarchy of low-, middle- and high-ranking apes.

The scientists then mapped out the reproductive histories of the 10 females, a difficult task for a long-lived and slow-breeding species like the chimpanzee. In their analysis, they counted as a success any offspring that survived to 5, the age of weaning. The group variability in fruitfulness proved significant.

Several of the low-ranking females had many pregnancies and births, but then lost most or all their infants, either to predation, poor nutrition, illness, accident, infanticide or causes unknown. By contrast, the highest-ranking female of the group, Fifi, is also the most successful mother. Now 38, Fifi has not lost a single one of her seven offspring. Five already are independent—including two sons in their 20s, a 16-year-old daughter who is herself a mother and a 12-year-old daughter who is pregnant—while the youngest two are on the cusp of weaning. The average age of reproductive maturity for a chimpanzee is 13, but the daughters of high-ranking females began breeding as young as 9.

The scientists do not yet know what distinguishes a high-ranking female from a subordinate, or why the offspring of dominant females fare better than those of the lowly. Dominant females are not any bigger or fleshier than their underlings, nor are they more overtly aggressive. High-rankers tend to be somewhat older than their subordinates, and a few females manage to gradually gain in stature as they age, but most stay put on the social pyramid no matter how long they live.

The scientists suspect that dominant females exert their pre-eminence in their choice of feeding terrains. Each female has her own turf that she forages through every day, and the dominants could be monopolizing the spots where the food is particularly nutritious. In addition, because feeding ranges overlap, the researchers theorize that should two females bump into each other while foraging, the high-status female gets first dibs on any good fruits or nuts that may be around.

"One thing we're trying to look at now is whether dominant females have a more steady body size," said Ms. Williams. "It could be that they don't lose weight in poor times." Fluctuations in body weight could affect fertility, lactation and the ability to fend off disease.

The scientists propose that a female's social rank is determined fairly early in life. Some daughters stay in their natal home, and may inherit their station from their mother, as Fifi did from her regal mother, Flo. More often, a young female will emigrate from her birthplace and join another group. It is during those early months of integration that a female makes her greatest effort to seek high status and is likeliest to engage other females in fights, or at least earnest, cacophonous discussions. After a while, a female appears to learn her place and from then on will grunt or be grunted at accordingly.

The researchers caution that the sample size in their study is extremely small, and that much more needs to be done to grasp the nuances of female competition in chimpanzees. Other research on primates has shown that dominant behavior, when taken to extremes, can backfire. Studying olive baboons, for example, Dr. Packer has found that the most dominant and aggressive females can suffer from fertility problems, possibly as a result of an excess of masculinizing hormones like testosterone.

Kathleen B. Kerr, a researcher and therapist at the Georgetown Family Center in Washington, has also been analyzing the Gombe data on female chimps as part of an effort to understand mother-infant relationships. She points out that while high rank for a chimpanzee is a critical factor in fostering successful motherhood, it is not the only factor. "There's variability between female chimps of the same rank in how they behave, what their life course is, and how many offspring they successfully raise," she said. "I don't think rank is [the] whole story."

In her observations, the chimpanzee mothers most adept at rearing young tend to be "very relaxed but conscientious," she said. They are vigilant yet calm, staying watchful for danger while encouraging their young to explore their surroundings. In comparison, the mothers with comparatively low success at raising babies to maturity "tend to be restrictive and overprotective of their offspring," she said, "which translates into the offspring being less confident and exploratory, and more restricted in their approach to the world."

It's an old story: The strong get stronger, while the weak get weaker—if they don't get eaten first.

THE NEW YORK TIMES

Tuesday, February 17, 1998

Road Maps of Apes

ASSOCIATED PRESS

Researchers studying apes in the wild have found that African bonobos use complex trail markers to communicate silently in the dense tropical forests where they live along the Congo River.

The discovery is contrary to the belief of many scientists that apes lack the brain structure for the use of symbolic language, E. Sue Savage-Rumbaugh of Georgia State University said on Saturday in a presentation to the American Association for the Advancement of Science.

Bonobos, apes that closely resemble chimpanzees, live in dense forests with faint trails in bands of more than 100 and each night rest together in trees in a different spot.

During the day, they separate into small groups and forage for food, often traveling for miles. When the day ends, they find their way back together at a new resting place.

Ms. Savage-Rumbaugh said that in following the animals, she noticed that whenever a trail crossed another trail, the lead group would stamp down vegetation or rip off large leaves and place them carefully.

"What they are doing is leaving little notes in the vegetation," she said. "Those notes are signals about where they are going to go."

To prove her discovery, Ms. Savage-Rumbaugh said she twice followed the trail signs far behind groups of the apes. At the end of each day, she found her way to the reassembled band's new nesting trees.

Ms. Savage-Rumbaugh said it is impossible to study verbal communications among bonobos in the wild because they vocalize only when they are together in the trees. But captive bonobos, she said, have been easily trained to respond to verbal language and to point to symbols that have specific meanings.

THE NEW YORK TIMES

Sunday, May 11, 1997

You Scratch My Back,
I'll Scratch Yours

BY DAVID PAPINEAU

Evolution by natural selection is a nasty business. Out there in the wild, animals of all kinds contend fiercely for scarce resources, and the meek leave no descendants to inherit their uncompetitive genes. But how then have we humans ended up so nice? True, we are not all saints, but it is a rare member of the species *Homo sapiens* who does not feel some impulse to lend a hand to those in need.

One ready answer would be that we are not slaves to our genes. We may indeed be products of biological evolution, separated from our chimpanzee cousins by a mere 5 million years of natural selection. But we are also creatures of culture, in whom civilization has instilled many characteristics that have nothing to do with animal competition. According to this way of thought, our niceness is just one of the many traits we get from our cultural nurture rather than our biological nature, along with literacy, litigiousness and a liking for rock 'n' roll.

However, the desire to explain human behavior in terms of evolution cannot be so quickly dismissed. The recent history of this idea testifies to its hardiness. Thirty years ago we had the "naked apes" and "territorial imperatives" of Desmond Morris and Robert Ardrey. Then there was E. O. Wilson and "sociobiology." The last few years have seen the emergence of an influential school of "evolutionary psychology." Whenever the biological approach seems about to collapse under the weight of criticism, it rises again with new strength, like a stubborn boxer whose efforts are only encouraged by each knockdown.

Modern advocates of the evolutionary approach have learned to avoid the mistakes of their predecessors. They no longer seek a direct biological meaning for every human foible, in the way that Desmond Morris would explain home decoration, say, as akin to a wolf marking its lair with its scent. Instead, contemporary "evolutionary psychologists" focus on the underlying mental mechanisms we have inherited from our evolutionary past. They accept that these mechanisms give rise to different patterns of behavior in different cultures. But at the same time, they argue, our inherited mentality places limits on what we can and cannot do. Any child can learn languages better than the best computer, but no human can beat a $2 calculator at multiplication. The obvious implication is that evolution has given us a mechanism for language, but none for mental arithmetic. More generally, our biological heritage means that some things come easily to humans, and others are very difficult.

Among the things that come easily to humans is niceness. Children don't have to be taught about good behavior. They catch on to concepts like sharing and playing fair almost before they can speak. But this brings us back to our original puzzle. How could humans possibly have evolved into such altruistic beings? If nice guys always finished last when our ancestors were scrabbling around for food on the African savanna, why does morality come so naturally to us now?

This is the question Matt Ridley aims to answer in *The Origins of Virtue*. Or, rather, he aims to provide a battery of answers. The evolution of altruism has been a topic of intense research for more than 20 years. While the biologically minded may still be a minority among social scientists, there are now enough of them to have produced a plethora of competing theories. Mr. Ridley is a distinguished British science journalist who proves an excellent guide to the current debate. Sometimes his eagerness to cover every angle means that different views are not always clearly distinguished, but he is never dull, and he illustrates the intricate logic of natural selection with many parables from ethology, anthropology and game theory.

Perhaps you are wondering why fancy logic is needed to explain altruism. Isn't the answer obvious? Wouldn't cooperative bands among our hunter-gatherer ancestors have fared better than individualists who tried to scratch out a living on their own? But this idea faces a telling objection. Although cooperation is undoubtedly beneficial, it is also evolutionarily unstable. It is open to exploitation by nasty mutants. Once an individual with selfish instincts is born into a hunter-gatherer band, it will take the benefit of any communal food but avoid the risk of catching it. So selfish individuals will leave more descendants, and soon enough the cooperative bands won't be cooperative anymore.

Still, given that we aren't all nasty nowadays, something must have prevented this outcome. The most popular theory is reciprocal altruism, more familiarly known as "You scratch my back, I'll scratch yours." Suppose that some of our ancestors evolved an instinct to share food only with those who share with them, or, for that matter, to scratch fleas off the backs of only those who scratch theirs. Then they would get the benefits of cooperation but would be immune to exploitation, because they'd simply stop helping those who didn't reciprocate. Mr. Ridley explains how a widely disseminated series of computer models has convinced most theorists that this kind of logrolling instinct can well be favored by natural selection.

However, it seems unlikely that this is the whole story about human niceness. Many humans give to charity without any prospect of a payback. To explain this, Mr. Ridley considers a converse question: Why are humans often so vengeful? What's the point of waging vendettas when they only bring trouble in their train? Well, maybe actually waging vendettas is a bad idea, but to be known for your vindictiveness can be a great advantage, for then people will take care not to cross you. And maybe the surest way of acquiring a reputation for vindictiveness is actually to be vindictive. So perhaps vengeful dispositions evolved not because it is advantageous to be vengeful, but because it is advantageous to be thought so. Similarly with generosity. Even if openhanded generosity is in itself costly, perhaps it is the best way to acquire a reputation for generosity, which will then pay off because it advertises you as someone who can be trusted in a deal.

In his final chapter Mr. Ridley draws some political conclusions from his biological analysis. The state should keep out of human affairs and leave smaller communities of property owners to look after themselves. Our natural inclinations toward trust and mutual aid will insure fairness within communities, but attempts by governments to make us go beyond these inclinations will only breed resistance. As Mr. Ridley puts it, "We are not so nasty that we need to be tamed by intrusive government, nor so nice that too much government does not bring out the worst in us."

There is plenty of room, however, to accept Mr. Ridley's style of evolutionary theorizing without embracing his political philosophy. One difficulty with his argument is illustrated by the bonobos, the so-called pygmy chimpanzees that live south of the Congo River. The recent history of this species shows that we can't simply jump from claims about our evolutionary history to conclusions about our current character. The bonobos probably separated from the other chimpanzees only about 1.5 million years ago. Yet their character and social organization are now strikingly different.

The bonobos are best known as the sexy chimpanzees. Their most striking idiosyncrasy is their readiness to use sex as a social lubricant. Any tension within a bonobo group is normally resolved by a quick orgy, in which they all have sex with one another, in all positions and combinations. Yet, as Frans de Waal explains in the elegant photo-essay *Bonobo: The Forgotten Ape*, this is just one way in which they diverge markedly from the other chimpanzees.

Mr. de Waal's book is designed more for the coffee table than the research library. The text is spiced with interviews with prominent bonobo experts and illustrated with Frans Lanting's spectacular photographs of bonobos in the wild. But at the same time it does an excellent job of describing what is now known about these elusive primates. Mr. de Waal, a professor of psychology at Emory University and Research Professor at the Yerkes Regional Primate Research Center in Atlanta, is himself a distinguished primatologist, and he explains in detail how a social gulf has arisen between bonobos and their chimpanzee cousins. Where chimpanzee bands are dominated by males and often tainted by infanticide, the bonobos conform far more closely to the model of the cuddly chimp, being female-centered, socially egalitarian and free from any serious violence.

The moral for Matt Ridley's argument is obvious. If such radical changes in chimpanzee psychology can arise within 1.5 million years, there might well be a similar gap between our hunter-gatherer past and modern human psychology. Any psychological traits produced by our evolution on the savanna a few million years ago could easily have been washed out again in the intervening ages.

Apart from this point, there is in any case another, more fundamental objection to Mr. Ridley's political conclusions. He seems to assume that the biologically natural way is necessarily the best way. But this is a mistake. It is arguable that war and philandering are in some sense biologically natural, but this does not make them right. Nor does it make them inevitable. Evolutionary psychologists like Mr. Ridley tend to forget that evolution has blessed humans with one special biological ability.

Unlike most other animals, we aren't just bags of reflexes; we are able to reflect on our circumstances and to figure out the best thing to do. Maybe the right course of action doesn't always come easily, but often we can manage it. When we need to do multiplication, for example, we can make the effort or, better, build a calculator. For all the biological sophistication of Mr. Ridley's ideas, they don't show that we shouldn't make an effort in the political realm too, and build systems of government that can channel our basic moral reflexes in more sophisticated directions.

THE NEW YORK TIMES

Sunday, June 1, 1997

Evolution and Morality

By Lionel Tiger

To the Editor:

In his thoughtful review of Matt Ridley's *Origins of Virtue* and Frans de Waal's *Bonobo* (May 11), David Papineau leaves a misleading impression when he comments that "if such radical changes in chimpanzee psychology can arise within 1.5 million years, there might well be a similar gap between our hunter-gatherer past and modern human psychology." But humans were hunter-gatherers almost exclusively until between 13,000 and 7,000 years ago, too brief a period for any significant evolutionary change, especially in such a fundamental matter as morality. In my book *The Manufacture of Evil*, I suggest that the reigning religious and moral systems of the planet emerged during the convulsive shift from hunting-gathering to agriculture and pastoralism. The ethics of small farmers and shepherds continue to prevail. There has developed no morality specific to the 10-generation-old industrial system.

THE NEW YORK TIMES

Sunday, January 26, 1997

Are Apes Naughty by Nature?

BY DAVID BERREBY

Frans de Waal likes to say that you don't have to be human to be humane. In the course of a 25-year career spent observing and recording the behavior of captive apes and monkeys, he has pioneered a new view of animal behavior that stands on its head the stereotype of apes as savage King Kongs. The C. H. Candler professor of primate behavior at Emory University and a behavioral researcher at the university's Yerkes Regional Primate Research Center, de Waal emphasizes that the mystery of aggression is yesterday's news—the concern of a post-World War II generation of scientists and intellectuals obsessed with the mass destruction they had witnessed. Now, he says, it's time to emphasize the other side of the coin, the side exhibited, for instance, by Binti Jua, the female gorilla who rescued a human toddler at a Chicago zoo last August.

In fact, de Waal says, all four species of great apes—the chimpanzee, the orangutan, the gorilla and the bonobo (the subject of his book, *Bonobo: The Forgotten Ape*, published by the University of California Press)—show reserves of empathy and kindness. So, for that matter, do monkeys and dolphins and dogs. De Waal portrays an animal kingdom in which the top chimp in a hierarchy is not the meanest or the baddest but the one with the best friendships and alliances, in which bonobos have heterosexual and homosexual sex as a way of cementing relationships and keeping the peace. If we want to understand what in nature makes us aggressive, de Waal says, we have to understand our equally deep instincts to get along.

It's a view with increasing influence among biologists and animal be-haviorists. "Up until about 1990, no one spoke in the scientific literature about affiliation," says Thomas Insel, director of the Yerkes center. "Now if you search in any data base, you can find scores of papers on the subject."

De Waal does not claim that apes are angels of peace. Chimpanzees, the species he has spent the most time observing, throw tantrums, go on ram-pages, occasionally kill one another. But, de Waal argues, that makes it all the more remarkable that most of the time, irritated chimpanzees keep their emo-tions in check, acting in ways you could call moderate and tolerant, ways you could call kind.

In a series of books written over the last 15 years, de Waal, who was born in the Netherlands in 1948 and received his Ph.D. in zoology from the University of Utrecht, has argued against what he calls "the old killer-ape myth" and its dark implications about human nature. Science, he maintains, has been biased by this long tradition of seeing morality as a thin veneer that human civilization spreads over blood-thirsty nature. "'Can animals re-ally have friends?' was the question of colleagues who without blinking ac-cepted that animals have rivals," he wrote in *Good Natured*, a book arguing that morality isn't opposed to our natural instincts but is instead an out-growth of them. Politicians have also been biased toward the dark, he says: "They will say the violence in Yugoslavia proves people are innately violent and cruel. They forget that people got along very well in Yugoslavia for 30 years before this conflict, and that fact also has to be taken into account. You might say my vision of nature is that it's a dog-refraining-from-eating-dog world."

That gift for imagery ("Male chimps entering an enclosure always puff up their hair to look big and powerful—like the corporate executive strid-ing into the board meeting") has given de Waal's work an impact outside his specialty, from Congress (where Newt Gingrich included de Waal's first book, *Chimpanzee Politics*, on the reading list he gave Republican freshmen in 1994) to psychology and psychiatry. His semipopular books marry data and speculation to compelling narratives about striking animal personali-ties. At the same time, the fundamental premise of de Waal's work—that what animals do can explain what humans do—remains a subject of bitter dispute.

For example, at a 1992 meeting, Frederick K. Goodwin, then head of the Alcohol, Drug Abuse and Mental Health Administration, noted that half of all male monkeys die violently before adulthood and said, "That is the natural way of it for males, to knock each other off." A few moments later he added, "Maybe it isn't just the careless use of the word when people call certain inner cities jungles." Goodwin was quickly attacked by the Congressional Black Caucus and other politicians and resigned. It wasn't just the racist con-notation you could see in the remark that sank him, but also the suggestion that human behavior could be explained by animals' conduct. Senator Edward

Kennedy and Representative John D. Dingell released a letter that said, "Primate research is a preposterous basis for discussing the crime and violence that plagues our country today."

Many cultural critics would agree. After all, what past generations have seen as natural—second-class status for women, racist societies—has turned out in retrospect to be a projection onto nature of what those societies believed. In *Primate Visions*, a book about the science and culture of primatology, Donna Haraway, a professor in the University of California at Santa Cruz's history of consciousness department, calls de Waal's portraits of chimpanzees a product of his time. He has depicted, she writes, a world where "primates became model yuppies."

Clever-sounding point, de Waal replies, but it depends on the notion that we can't know anything about animals except our own preconceptions. A good experiment can show that animal relationships are real, not just a projection of the researcher's psyche. For instance, in a series of experiments in 1995, de Waal and his students would put two capuchin monkeys (a species that primatologists sometimes call South America's version of the Chimpanzee) into separate test chambers side by side, with only mesh between them. They'd then give one animal a bowl of apples. Repeatedly, the monkeys found ways to share the food through the mesh. But putting different combinations of monkeys in the experiment also proved that this sharing is a deliberate choice: Monkeys that don't like each other don't share food.

"Cognitive ethology" of the kind de Waal studies also has its detractors among scientists. Unlike critics in the humanities camp, biologists accept the accuracy of reports of interesting and varied animal behavior. But, they argue, we don't understand evolution, or the biology of development, well enough to extrapolate anything about the biology of human behavior. How do we know, for instance, which animal to take as a model? The rat? The monkey? Even among our closest relatives, there are enormous differences in behavior. Take the male-dominated chimpanzees, with their occasional bouts of sex, and the more egalitarian bonobos, which initiate some kind of social-sexual contact every hour and a half on average. (In *Bonobo*, de Waal says that chimp kisses "are rather platonic," while those of bonobos are intense. One zookeeper used to chimps accepted a kiss from a bonobo. "Was he taken aback when he suddenly felt the ape's tongue in his mouth!") The sexual habits of the two species couldn't be more different, and they don't much resemble those of human beings. The 5 million years of evolution that separate humans and the chimp-bonobo line is a long time.

De Waal acknowledges the difference among species but stresses that if humans, chimps and even monkeys show signs of empathy, it suggests that empathy arose in some common ancestor—that it is, in short, part of our shared heritage, like anger or sexual desire. "If I can explain chimpanzee behavior as identical in its motivations to human behavior, and you say it isn't, I think the burden is on you to show why they're not the same," de Waal says. "There has been so much underestimating of animal cognition that to perhaps overestimate it, as I probably do, is probably a healthy reaction."

In any event, it's certainly true that many have been persuaded by de Waal's narratives of ape anguish and ecstasy. Roberta M. Gilbert, a psychiatrist who practices in Falls Church, Va., and teaches at the Georgetown Family Center in Washington, says that de Waal's books have helped her to become a better therapist. "After all, what gives us all of our problems is not our thinking but our emotions, and chimps live in the very same emotional world that you and I live in."

Perhaps it's true, as de Waal's critics say, that tough-minded reasoning can prove such an intuition wrong. But it's impossible to resist the sense of common emotional ground when de Waal stands before one of the Yerkes center's two chimp enclosures and softly calls, "Hey, hey, hey" in his lightly accented tenor. In a moment Donna, a 6-year-old chimp, is swinging herself toward him on her hands, past tire rims, stretched fire hoses and other chimp toys. She puts a couple of fingers through the fence, and de Waal rubs his thick finger against her two huge knuckles, which are caked in their seams with red Georgia clay. Then he delicately strokes her chin. Her mouth open in a loose-lipped, relaxed smile and her eyes looking off in the distance with the thoughtfully vacant expression of an ape at ease, Donna pushes her face outward for this gesture of trust.

But now Klaus comes rushing over. A big-eared, toddler-size 2-year-old with wary eyes the color of apricot jam, he leaps onto an upended barrel to Donna's left, raking a piece of white plastic pipe against the chain link and swaying rhythmically from side to side. Suddenly he leaps to the ground and pirouettes back up, throwing himself full force into the fence. It shakes when he slams into it and shudders with a metallic shick-shick-shick as he hangs by three slender limbs and resumes dragging the pipe across the fence with the fourth. Ratcheta-ratcheta-ratcheta.

Without taking her eyes off de Waal, Donna stretches out her left arm and grips Klaus firmly by the ankle. A quiet, unagitated gesture, as if to say, "Shhh, I'm trying to concentrate." The little ape stops for a moment. He looks at Donna. She lets go. He starts up again. As de Waal strokes Donna's chin, she reaches out again for Klaus's ankle. The same gesture. Force and kindness balanced on a fine edge of judgment, a path keenly chosen between all-out rage and submission to a toddler's whim. Not human, for sure. But it certainly looks humane.

Sunday, October 27, 1996

Going Ape

BY MARK RIDLEY

"Godi, slowly raising himself, screaming with fear and anguish, watched his tormentors go. There were appalling wounds on his face, body and limbs. He was heavily bruised. He bled from dozens of gashes, cuts and punctures. He was never seen again.... He surely died." Godi was a male chimpanzee in the Kahama group at Gombe, Tanzania; he was put to death in 1974 by a gang of males from the neighboring Kasekela group, in an event that (as much as any) led anthropologists and biologists to reimagine chimpanzees and to do the work that makes possible, 20 years later, *Demonic Males*, by Richard Wrangham and Dale Peterson.

Jane Goodall had been studying the Kasekela chimpanzees at Gombe for a decade, and (as Mr. Wrangham and Mr. Peterson describe it) the initial picture of social life had been peaceful. Perhaps things were too comfortable. The group grew and started to split, forming a colony (which was to become the Kahama group) to the north. The split was gradual: It was just statistically detectable in the mid-1960s and was not complete until 1973. The rupture was the great drama in the area when Mr. Wrangham arrived in Gombe to begin his graduate work in 1970, as there had already been some mysterious disappearances. Nothing was really witnessed, however, until Ms. Goodall's senior field assistant at her research center followed the raid on Godi. When the new colony was hived off, violent rivalry was born.

Many chimpanzees have suffered Godi's fate since 1974, and such violence is undoubtedly part of normal chimpanzee social behavior. By 1977 the Kahama group had been exterminated: All the males were killed and the females were either killed or transferred to the Kasekela group. But Macht-politik, the rule of force, is cruel: With the Kahama out of the way, the Kaseke-lans' new neighbors were the powerful Kalande—and now the ranks of the Kasekela started to thin.

Mr. Wrangham, a professor of anthropology at Harvard, and Mr. Peter-son, a science writer, describe the chimpanzees as killing "deliberately." It is difficult enough for us to judge the deliberations of our fellow humans—"We have," as King Charles I counterproverbially observed, "no window into men's souls"—and the uncertainties multiply for chimpanzees. What is striking, however, is the characteristic behavior of the chimpanzees about to launch a raid. They "traveled purposefully" and "maintained an unusual silence"; they picked off temporarily isolated individuals. An experienced researcher can tell when a raid is on. Some critics will hold out for a purely mental, in-tentionalist definition of murder, but most readers will be persuaded by the behavioral evidence alone that raids like the one on Godi are deliberate killing, amounting to murder. If a jury can convict a dumb human of murder, so can it judge chimpanzees.

Demonic Males is about human as well as nonhuman male violence, and about violence directed against females as well as against males. The authors discuss modern genocide, anthropological work on violence, and the ten-dency of artists (like Herman Melville and Paul Gauguin) and social scientists (like Margaret Mead) to invent Edens of free love on islands of the Pacific. The purpose of Mr. Wrangham and Mr. Peterson is to argue for evolutionary con-tinuity of male violence from apes (or earlier ancestors) to humans, and to use a similar kind of Darwinian explanation to understand male violence in all these species. Of course, human violence has cultural causes too, and these authors sensibly dismiss the simple biology-culture division. Thus, the high homicide rate in American, as compared to European, cities, has an obvious nonbiological cause—guns. But homicide rates in different societies have a rather constant sex ratio (men kill at about 20 times the rate that women do) and age-distribution profile, even though the absolute rates vary more than a thousandfold. It is tempting to see an evolutionary signal in those reg-ularities, notwithstanding cultural variation.

I find the case for evolutionary continuity convincing, and it is im-portant, intellectually, for understanding ourselves and the rest of nature. The book is written for a general educated audience, and belongs to the emerging genre of serious scientific books that have something to say about questions of interest to many people, not just to specialists. It is enjoyable and easy to read. The authors, I suspect, take a certain Machiavellian plea-sure in describing with little or no comment red claws and teeth. They leave their readers to do much of the moralizing for themselves; many will be eager to do so.

If we grant an evolutionary continuity of violence, what difference does it make? I fear that one common answer would be that it suggests violence is inevitable: inevitable because (it is believed) biological causes are more fixed and unalterable than social causes. Mr. Wrangham and Mr. Peterson would reject that answer. Biological causes are not in general any more rigid than other kinds of cause; biological systems are often flexible and social systems reactionary. The main answer to the question of what difference it makes, if you know that human violence has an evolutionary ancestry, then has to be "not much." If you want to reduce levels of human violence you would probably make much the same recommendations either way.

But evolutionary knowledge is not useless. We have been so unsuccessful in controlling violence, and the problem is so important, that it is foolish to ignore any clues, particularly if they come from a theory as well worked out as evolution. Evolutionary theory also suggests factors that influence the level of violence. The genetic relatedness between individuals is about the first thing an evolutionary theorist would look at, but it was ignored until 1988, when two evolutionists turned to the problem.

Mr. Wrangham and Mr. Peterson themselves consider the lessons from a species of apparently "gentle" apes, the bonobos. Bonobos are close relatives of chimpanzees, and of us. They are little studied, but what evidence there is suggests they have low levels of violence. How do they manage it? The key, in the account given here, is strong bonds among females, so that trouble-seeking males are kept in place by prompt displays of female solidarity. Bonds among females are, for various reasons, weak in chimpanzees. In bonobos, female relationships are cemented by the agreeable practice of hoka-hoka, or "genito-genital rubbing." Tame males, sorority, lesbian sex—it sounds like the kind of paradise that some modern campus dweller might invent. I wonder what odds Mr. Wrangham and Mr. Peterson would offer that the bonobo idyll will survive more extensive research. But meanwhile the bonobos offer a more inspiring prospect than our grim late 20th-century government budgets, with their more generous allocations for prisons than for universities.

How Did Man Get So Bad?
Looking to the Apes

By Christopher Lehmann-Haupt

Of all the species, only humans deliberately seek out and kill their own, or so it was widely believed among scientists until the early afternoon of Jan. 7, 1974. Then, as Richard Wrangham and Dale Peterson report in *Demonic Males: Apes and the Origins of Human Violence*, a significant event occurred.

In Gombe National Park in Tanzania, eight chimpanzees purposefully traveled to the border of their range, entered a neighboring chimpanzee territory, attacked and mortally wounded a young male from another community, then returned home.

This was "the first recorded instance of lethal raiding among chimpanzees," the authors write, "and among chimpanzee observers and animal scientists in general, it struck a momentous chord." This chord reverberates in *Demonic Males*. Mr. Wrangham is a professor of anthropology at Harvard, and Mr. Peterson is a popular writer on primate behavior, two of his eight previous books being *Chimpanzee Travels: On and Off the Road in Africa* and *Visions of Caliban: On Chimpanzees and People*, written with Jane Goodall. In the present book, the authors explore the complex implications of the killing with acuteness and eloquence.

The event was significant not only as an example of another species that killed its own deliberately, but also because the species happened to be the one most closely related to humans. But was it typical, the authors ask, or an aberration? If it was typical, "did it imply that human killing is rooted in prehuman history?" Both time and further exploration would tell.

As *Demonic Males* reveals, the killing turned out to be far from isolated. Thanks to the "revolution in observing" that began in the 1960s, students of primate behavior eventually saw it as part of a pattern of ape behavior that includes murderous raiding, the battering and rape of females, and infanticide, although what the benefits might be to the various species involved has not yet become entirely clear.

What's more, Mr. Wrangham and Mr. Peterson point out, the connection between primate and human behavior has come to be seen more clearly. First, DNA analysis has confirmed how closely related humans are to chimpanzees, indeed that chimps are closer to humans than they are to gorillas! Such analysis makes it possible to estimate that our common ancestor with the chimpanzee existed as recently as 5 million years ago.

Second, the authors argue, recent anthropology has shown how widespread and consistent throughout human civilization is "a system of intense, male-initiated territorial aggression, including lethal raiding into neighboring communities in search of vulnerable enemies to attack and kill." Despite quests for utopian societies by the likes of the painter Gauguin, the novelist Melville and the anthropologist Margaret Mead, and despite the argument that violence is an invention of Western civilization, the fact is inescapable that humans are universally killers, *Demonic Males* concludes.

One obvious objection to all this is that while their behavior may appear similar, apes and humans act for different reasons: Many argue that the former kills instinctively, whereas the latter makes war for calculated reasons. One might protest too that the authors' rationalizations of the genetic benefits of primate violence sometimes sound far-fetched (particularly the explanation of why a female gorilla might be impressed by a male who killed her young). And that in detailing the stories of Gauguin's sojourn in Tahiti and Melville's experiences in the Marquesas Islands, Mr. Wrangham and Mr. Peterson wander a little wide of their main point.

The authors concede some of these objections. They admit their explanations for ape behavior are at times "Just So Stories" that fit the facts but haven't been proved. They emphasize that culture can and often must supersede instinct: that just because apes commit rape in no way justifies similar behavior in humans.

Yet at the same time, they warn against the error committed by Francis Galton, Darwin's cousin, when he drew a binary distinction between nature and nurture. In fact, as they persuasively illustrate, a lot of thought goes into the most instinctive of chimp behavior, and a lot of instinct goes into the most rational of human decisions. What is basically at stake in both camps is pride, they say, which is often why wars are fought. Simple as that.

In casting about for ways that might free us from our evolutionary bind, the authors describe a recently discovered ape species, the bonobo, or pygmy chimpanzee, that along with chimpanzees "evolved from the same ancestor that gave rise to humans," yet "is one of the most peaceful, unaggressive species of mammals living on the earth today." Part of their point in describing the bonobo seems to be to show how close in evolutionary terms we humans came to being a peaceful, sex-loving species with little interest in the violent quest for status.

Yet at the same time they imply that the very habits of violence that distinguish us from the bonobos, like a lust for high status and a taste for meat, are precisely what helped us to evolve into humans. Thus our dilemma as they depict it is classically tragic, and the only way out is through the application of rigorously self-conscious human intelligence: an intelligence willing to confront what Arthur Koestler once called "the ghost in the machine" and an intelligence able to accept the implications of a book like the one Mr. Wrangham and Mr. Peterson have written.

THE NEW YORK TIMES

Tuesday, April 14, 1998

A Conversation with Emily Sue Savage-Rumbaugh: She Talks to Apes and, According to Her, They Talk Back

BY CLAUDIA DREIFUS

Dr. Emily Sue Savage-Rumbaugh, 52, a researcher at Georgia State University in Decatur, Ga., studies communication among primates and runs a 55-acre laboratory near Atlanta where she trains animals and humans to communicate with each other.

She is the author of *Kanzi: The Ape at the Brink of the Human Mind*, and, with Stuart G. Shanker and Talbot J. Taylor, is a co-author of *Ape Language and the Human Mind*, to be published next month by Oxford University Press.

Q. Do your apes speak?

A. They don't speak. They point to printed symbols on a keyboard. Their vocal tract isn't like ours, and they don't make human noises. However, they do make all kinds of ape noises. And I believe they use them to communicate with one another. Now, the apes may not always elect to talk about the same things we do. They might not have a translation for every word in our vocabulary to theirs. But from what I've seen, I believe they are communicating very complex things.

Let me give you an example. A few weeks ago, one of our researchers, Mary Chiepelo was out in the yard with Panbanisha. Mary thought she heard a squirrel and so she took the keyboard and said, 'There's a squirrel.' And Panbanisha said 'DOG.' Not very much later, three dogs appeared and headed in the direction of the building where Kanzi was.

Mary asked Panbanisha, 'Does Kanzi see the dogs?' And Panbanisha looked at Mary and said, 'A-frame.' A-frame is a specific sector of the forest here that has an A-frame hut on it. Mary later went up to 'A-frame' and found the fresh footprints of dogs everywhere at the site. Panbanisha knew where they were without seeing them.

And that seems to be the kind of information that apes transmit to each other: 'There's a dangerous animal around. It's a dog and it's coming towards you.'

Q. Your apes watch a great deal of TV—why?

A. Because their lives are so confined. They can expand their world by watching television.

Q. What do they watch?

A. This varies. They like the home videos we make about events happening to people they know from around the lab. They like suspenseful stories, with an interesting resolution. Of movies we buy, they really like films about human beings trying to relate to some kind of ape-like creatures. So they like 'Tarzan,' 'Iceman,' 'Quest for Fire,' the Clint Eastwood movies with the orangutan.

Q. You have a game with the apes, 'Monster,' where a lab staffer dresses up in a gorilla suit and feigns being frightful. Why?

A. It's a game started some years ago when we were working with two chimps, Sherman and Austin. We discovered that if someone dressed up in a gorilla suit and we drove this 'monster' off with poundings of hammers and sticks, we upped our status with the chimps. In other words, 'We're not the experimenters, in charge. We're your helpers.' Sherman and Austin didn't know we were playing. For a while Kanzi and Panbanisha didn't either. But they caught on soon enough and now they love the game....

... Another time, Panbanisha and I were walking around the building where Sherman and Mercury, this male chimpanzee with a big interest in Panbanisha, lives. Mercury came outside and was being really bad, displaying, throwing bark, and spitting at Panbanisha. So Panbanisha opened her backpack, where there was a gorilla mask inside and she pointed to symbols on the keyboard and asked Mary to play 'Monster.' Mary did that, and Mercury flew indoors.

Panbanisha was able to use the game to stop him from displaying at her. She knew it was pretend. He didn't.

Q. How do you know when the chimps point to symbols on the keyboard that they are not just pointing to any old thing?

A. We test Kanzi and Panbanisha by either saying English words or showing them pictures. We know that they can find the symbol that corresponds to the word or the picture. If we give similar tests to their siblings who haven't learned language, they fail.

Many times, we can verify through actions. For instance, if Kanzi says 'Apple chase,' which means he wants to play a game of keep away with an apple, we say, 'Yes, let's do.' And then, he picks up an apple and runs away and smiles at us.

Q. Some of your critics say that all your apes do is mimic you?

A. If they were mimicking me, they would repeat just what I'm saying, and they don't. They answer my questions. We also have data that shows that only about two percent of their utterances are immediate imitations of ours.

Q. Nonetheless, many in the scientific community accuse you of over-interpreting what your apes do.

A. There are *some* who say that. But none of them have been willing to come spend some time here. I've tried to invite critics down here. None have taken me up on it. I've invited Tom Sebeok (of Indiana University) personally and he never responded. I think his attitude was something to the effect that, 'It's so clear that what is happening is either cued, or in some way over-interpreted, that a visit is not necessary.' I would assume that many of the people associated with the Chomskyian perspective including Noam Chomsky himself have the same approach: that there's no point in observing something they're certain doesn't exist.

Their belief is that there is a thing called human language and that unless Kanzi does everything a human can, he doesn't have it. They refuse to consider what Kanzi does, which is comprehend, as language. And it's not even a matter of disagreeing over what Kanzi does. It's a matter of disagreeing over what to call these facts. They are asking Kanzi to do everything that humans do, which is specious. He'll never do that. It still doesn't negate what he can do.

Q. Your husband, Dr. Duane M. Rumbaugh, is a distinguished comparative psychologist who is a pioneer in the study of ape language. Has your research been helped by the fact that your personal life is so fused with your professional life?

A. Without our being together, I don't think that one could ever be responsible for as many apes as we have here. Duane and I live right near the research center and we're willing to go there day and night, 365 days a year. If an ape is sick, if one of the apes has gotten free, if Panbanisha is frightened because she's heard the river's about to flood, we go.

There have been lots of frictions, though. Duane was very, very upset when I began taking the apes out of their cages. And when I began to say that Lana (Duane's chimp) didn't understand some of the things she was saying and that comprehension of language was important, not just production—we almost broke up over that.

But we really love each other, and we're united in our core beliefs: that there is a huge capacity on the part of apes and probably all kinds of other animals that's being ignored. By ignoring it, humans are separating ourselves from the natural world we've evolved from. The bonobos are a real bridge to that world. At base, no matter how much Duane and I argue, we both know this is true.

THE NEW YORK TIMES

Tuesday, April 28, 1998

Ancestral Humans Could Speak, Anthropologists' Finding Suggests

BY JOHN NOBLE WILFORD

While scientists agree that speech is probably the most important behavioral attribute that distinguishes human beings from other animals, they have been at a loss to determine when and how that transforming evolutionary step occurred.

They have probed the human brain and compared it with casts of the braincase from ancient fossil skulls. They have compared bones and muscle attachment points in the throats of humans, apes and ancestral human skeletons. Archeologists have examined patterns in early stone tools for clues to when humans might have developed the creativity and the self-awareness usually associated with communication skills like speech.

All they had been able to agree on is that the earliest unambiguous evidence for human speech is found in the cave art and other artifacts, particularly in Europe and Africa, that began appearing some 40,000 years ago.

Now scientists at Duke University have explored a new avenue of fossil anatomy and found surprising evidence suggesting that vocal capabilities like those of modern humans may have evolved among species of the *Homo* line more than 400,000 years ago.

By then, their research shows, human ancestors may have had a full modern complement of the nerves leading to the muscles of the tongue and so could have been capable of forming speech sounds.

The new findings, moreover, indicate that the Neanderthals, relatives of modern humans, could have had the same gift for speech. Their extinction about 30,000 years ago has often been attributed in part to speech deficiencies, restricting their ability for cultural innovation.

In a report being published today in *The Proceedings of the National Academy of Sciences*, the Duke anthropologists say that if their interpretation involving the tongue nerves is correct, "then humanlike speech capabilities may have evolved much earlier than has been inferred from the archeological evidence for the antiquity of symbolic thought."

The research was conducted by Dr. Richard F. Kay and Dr. Matt Cartmill at the Duke Medical Center in Durham, N.C., with the assistance of a former student, Michelle Balow. The results were also described earlier this month in Salt Lake City at a meeting of the American Association of Physical Anthropology.

"This is evidence for the proposition that Neanderthals could talk," Dr. Cartmill said.... "Did they sound like modern humans? I don't know."

Anthropologists familiar with the research said the findings were interesting and exciting. Some were reserving judgment, but not Dr. Erik Trinkaus, an anthropologist at Washington University in St. Louis, who specializes in Neanderthal studies.

"I think it's not only a reasonable conclusion," he said, "but one long overdue."

Dr. Trinkaus said previous research had been based on deficient anatomical reconstructions, none of which adequately took into account the neurological aspects for controlling the vocal tract to allow for speech. As for the possibility of speech by archaic *Homo sapiens* 400,000 years ago, even before Neanderthals, he said this was consistent with a significant enlargement of brain size in that period, the appearance of a more complex tool technology and migrations into colder climates, where life probably depended on greater planning that could be related to advances in communications skills.

On the other side, Dr. Philip Lieberman of Brown University, an authority on early language, has argued that the Neanderthal throat would not have been well suited for the production of the vowels a, i and u. But Dr. Trinkaus contended that a species would not have needed to produce all those sounds in order to have speech and language.

Even the discovery in Israel a decade ago of a Neanderthal skeleton with a large hyoid bone, which is in the throat and associated with speech, had not settled the issue of Neanderthal speech. Scientists had said there was still insufficient fossil evidence to enable an understanding of how the large hyoid bone might have influenced the production of vocalizations.

Dr. Cartmill himself cautioned that the new evidence for earlier human speech "is suggestive, but, in the present state of our knowledge, it is not proof."

Other scientists noted that other, independent evolutionary developments, including a lengthened larynx, enlarged prefrontal brain lobes and some reconfigurations of the brain, would have been critical to the emergence of speech. The size of the brain of Neanderthals was well within the range of that of modern humans.

The Duke scientists directed their research at the hypoglossal canal, a hole at the bottom of the skull in the back, where the spinal cord connects to the brain. Through the canal run nerve fibers from the brain to the muscles of the tongue.

It occurred to the scientists that the size of the hypoglossal canal might serve as an index of the vocal abilities of modern and early humans. The wider the canal, they assumed, the more nerve fibers there could be to control the tongue muscles. And the more nerves, they suggested, the finer control the species could have over its tongue for the purpose of making speech sounds.

The researchers compared measurements of hypoglossal canals of modern humans, apes and several human ancestor fossils, and concluded that the canals of modern humans are almost twice as large as those of modern apes—the chimpanzee and the gorilla—which are incapable of speech. They also found that the canal size of australopithecines, earlier human relatives that died out about 1 million years ago, did not differ much from that of chimpanzees.

The results, the scientists reported, "suggest minimum and maximum dates for the appearance of the modern human pattern of tongue motor innervation and speech abilities."

To narrow the range, the scientists examined skeletons of Neanderthals and also of species of the *Homo* genus that lived as much as 400,000 years ago. These included Kabwe specimens from Africa and Swanscombe fossils from Europe. Their hypoglossal canals fell within the range of those of modern *Homo sapiens*.

"By the time we get to the Kabwe, about 400,000 years ago, you get a canal that's a modern size," Dr. Cartmill said. "And that's true of all later *Homo* species, including Neanderthal."

THE NEW YORK TIMES

Sunday, May 3, 1998

Look Who's Talking;
Don't Bother Listening

By John Noble Wilford

So ancestors of human beings might have had the capability to speak as early as 400,000 years ago, as anthropologists reported last week. But what did they have to say? Probably much more than an occasional yabba dabba doo.

They may have huddled around an open fire and cursed Og for letting a choice mammoth get away. Or they shivered in a rock shelter and talked over plans to move south for the winter, following the game. Even then, weather was a conversational standby: My, my, aren't winters colder now than in olden times?

Anthropologists suspect there was something else familiar about ancestral chitchat. They probably gossiped a lot about family, social relationships, sickness and death. If that poor young mother dies, who will take care of her baby? Is the head of the clan the hunter he once was? Is your son interested in my daughter? Perhaps Og was mooning over that woman in the neighboring clan when he should have had his mind on that mammoth.

What the earliest speaking ancestors spoke about is hardly a frivolous question. It may reflect the evolutionary root of language and speech, behavior critical in setting humans apart from other animals.

What they said, though, was less important to the scientists than when they actually said it. The scientists at Duke University last week announced that they explored a new avenue of fossil anatomy and found surprising evidence suggesting that these vocal abilities may have evolved earlier than previously thought. The much-maligned Neanderthal could probably speak, though perhaps not well enough to ward off extinction 30,000 years ago.

"When you look around us, only one animal has language and speech," said Dr. Matt Cartmill, an anthropologist at Duke University, whose work with Dr. Richard F. Kay and a former student, Michelle Balow, was published last week in The Proceedings of the National Academy of Sciences. "That permits us to have a power over the world that no other animal has."

Ancestors as far back as *Homo erectus* more than a million years ago had developed a brain about 80 percent the size of the human brain and probably had a lot on their minds before they had the vocal equipment to utter their thoughts and feelings. They were beginning to live in larger groups, sharing work and responsibilities, dealing with increasingly complex social relations by imposing symbolic meaning on reality. Their brains—scientists see a correlation between brain size and the size of living groups—thus could have been capable of language before they could speak a word.

The connection between social relations and speech is the reason Dr. Robin Dunbar, a British anthropologist, thinks it very likely that primeval conversation was spiced with gossip, antecedents of the kaffeeklatsch and talk shows.

The new research by the Duke physical anthropologists has revived debate about the origin and timing of human speech. Whether *Homo erectus*, a significant transition species between primitive and more recent human ancestors, could speak is problematic. The earliest unequivocal evidence for human speech is the cave art and other artifacts of modern *Homo sapiens*, beginning some 40,000 years ago. Imagine the critics coming and going at Lascaux and speaking of some cave Michelangelo.

In any event, the cave painters left the first clear expressions of symbolic thought and a strong argument for speech as a recent development.

But the Duke researchers found anatomical evidence suggesting that vocal capabilities like those of modern humans may have evolved in archaic *Homo sapiens*, including Neanderthals. They compared the diameter of a hole at the bottom of the skulls in modern humans, apes and several earlier species of the genus *Homo*.

The hole is the hypoglossal canal through which nerve fibers from the brain pass to control muscles of the tongue. Measurements showed that the passage in modern human skulls is twice the width of those in speechless chimpanzees and some of the more distant human ancestors. But in 400,000-year-old fossils of the *Homo* line, the hypoglossal canals fell within the size range of modern humans and thus could have carried enough nerves for tongues to form speech sounds. It is only suggestive evidence, not proof, but enough to intrigue other scientists.

More Than Dada

One problem, Dr. Cartmill said, is sorting out the physical attributes crucial to speech. The position of the larynx, the voice box, is undoubtedly important. In apes it sits high in the neck. It is lower in humans, which facilitates the utterance of a wide range of sounds but makes people the only mammals incapable of simultaneously drinking and breathing.

If the content of ancestral talk was familiar, the sounds may have been less so, outside the nursery. Infants are born with a high larynx, which limits their ability to form any but the simplest word sounds like goo, dada, mamma. Only when the larynx descends do they develop fluency. Perhaps, anthropologists say, early ancestors were similarly restricted. Vowel sounds like e, a and o are characteristic of all languages today, suggesting deep origins.

Dr. Philip Lieberman, a cognitive scientist at Brown University, who wrote *Eve Spoke* (Norton, 1998), imagines early speech as short, simple words strung together in short phrases or sentences uttered slowly. Studying children, he noted that they talk about 50 percent more slowly than adults until about the age of 10. It is "a reasonable guess," he said, that the same applied to early ancestors.

Dr. Ian Tattersall, an evolutionary biologist at the American Museum of Natural History in New York City and author of *Becoming Human* (Harcourt and Brace, 1998), also looks to children as possible models of how language and speech developed. At first, their sounds are elemental, crying, laughing and grunting. With growth and experience, undifferentiated connections in their brains are "rewired" with new pathways permitting speech of increasing complexity. This may be one reason, he said, that learning a new language becomes much more difficult after the age of 10.

Whoever had the first word, even the Duke scientists realize theirs will not be the last word on the origin of human speech.

THE NEW YORK TIMES

Tuesday, January 13, 1998

Brain of Chimpanzee Sheds Light on Mystery of Language

BY SANDRA BLAKESLEE

A surprising new study reveals that chimpanzees have a structure in their brains that is similar to a so-called "language center" in human brains, challenging cherished notions of how language evolved in humans and why apes cannot talk.

In most people, the structure, a slender inch-long piece of tissue called the planum temporale, is larger in the left side of the brain than the right. Since this area is involved in the processing and comprehension of speech sounds and sign language, scientists concluded 30 years ago that an enlarged plenum temporale in the left hemisphere was required for language and may have evolved for this purpose. Until now, no other animal was shown to have the same asymmetry in this brain region, located at the side of the head and connected to the ears.

The study, published in the current issue of the journal *Science*, was carried out by three anthropologists—Dr. Patrick Gannon of the Mount Sinai School of Medicine in New York, Dr. Ralph Holloway of Columbia University, Dr. Douglas Broadfield of the City University of New York—and Dr. Allen Braun, a neurologist at the National Institute on Deafness and Other Communication Disorders in Bethesda, Md.

"This is an interesting and useful finding," said Dr. Antonio Damasio, an expert on brain and language at the University of Iowa College of Medicine in Iowa City. It shows the dangers of concentrating on brain centers and areas, he said, and supports recent research showing that language is widely distributed in the brain and probably evolved from novel connections rather than from new structures.

Language evolution remains a profound mystery. Sometime within the last 2 million years, two-legged primates, or hominids, developed the ability to talk with words, a dazzlingly difficult skill, said Dr. Terrence Deacon, a biological anthropologist at Boston University and McLean Hospital at Harvard Medical School.

Language requires lightning-fast processing of speech and understanding of abstract symbols—traits that other animals seem not to possess to the degree that humans do, he said. One can imagine the brain undergoing important reorganizations that underlie the ability to argue, cajole, complain and pontificate.

In the late 1960s, scientists were strongly influenced by the idea that bigger is better and that evolutionary pressures would lead to obvious structural changes in the human brain, Dr. Deacon said. If they could find unique bits of human brain architecture, they concluded, it might explain language. A study conducted in 1968 seemed to confirm this view, Dr. Deacon said. Of 100 human brains examined, 68 had an enlarged left planum temporale, 24 had structures of equal size and 11 had larger plana temporale on the right side.

Many people took this to mean that the planum temporale might be a "control center" for language, Dr. Gannon said. It is part of the auditory association cortex where sounds come in from the ear, are processed and sent to other parts of the brain. Further evidence stemmed from links between the planum temporale and "a melange of behaviors and disorders including musical talent, handedness and schizophrenia," Dr. Gannon said.

A few years ago, Dr. Gannon and his colleagues were examining preserved chimpanzee brains with the same methods used in the 1968 study. "We were simply exploring, looking for asymmetries, when one day our eyes popped out," he said. Of 18 chimpanzee brains examined, 17 had enlarged plana temporale on the left side of the brain. "This was more pronounced than in humans," Dr. Gannon said in a telephone interview.

Because chimpanzees cannot talk or play the violin, what does the finding mean? Aside from the obvious fact that the common ancestor of chimpanzees and humans had this brain asymmetry 8 million years ago, Dr. Gannon said there are three possibilities.

First, the asymmetry in the common ancestor is unrelated to language or communication. But later on, humans built on it and evolved the unique capacity for language. The planum temporale in chimpanzees did not evolve along the same path and plays an unknown role.

Second, the ancestral planum temporale is involved with communication but followed different trajectories in the two species. In humans it laid the basis for spoken and sign language and in chimps it laid the basis for a more gesture-based language.

"Chimps may have their own sophisticated form of language that we fail to recognize," Dr. Gannon said. "They have sense of self, can deceive one another, and show many complex communicative behaviors. Our language is vocal and auditory. Their language is gestural and visual."

The third possibility is that the planum temporale is not directly related to language or communication but has tangential functions, and its role in language has been vastly overrated.

"I think this study provides a strong demonstration that this particular brain asymmetry is not likely to be crucial for language," said Dr. Deacon, whose book *The Symbolic Species* (Norton, 1997) lays out modern theories of language evolution. It supports the idea that humans did not evolve new brain structures for language but used structures that were present in other animals, he said.

To find out how language really evolved, researchers are looking more at microcircuitry than at gross anatomy, Dr. Deacon said. After all, 30 of every 100 people on average do not show the asymmetry, yet they appear to use language just like everyone else.

Studies show that there is tremendous variability in where language ends up in each person's brain, he said, and it can even move around in young adulthood after injury or, as one study showed, in learning how to do simultaneous translations. In that study, one language stayed on the left and the second language literally shifted to the right side of brain.

Better answers about language evolution lie in the way regions are connected in the brain, said Dr. Jeffrey Hutsler, a research assistant professor at Dartmouth College in Hanover, N.H., who dissects human brains to look for such clues. Patches of connected cells in so-called language areas are laid out differently in the left and right sides of the brain, he said. Such structural variations could lead to different firing rates among cells, making some better at processing fast speech sounds.

In the meantime, no one has a clue about the function of the large left planum temporale in chimpanzees. They may use it for hearing calls and hoots and other sounds, Dr. Gannon said, or they may have traits that are on the threshold of human abilities.

"Madam, I'm Adam"

By Derek Bickerton

What language really is, and how it began, are questions that have yet to receive satisfactory answers. Attempts to find them date at least to the Pharaoh Psamtik, who isolated two newborns in a cave (with a deaf caregiver) to see what, if anything, they would eventually say. Why should these questions prove more intractable than those about human ancestry, the nature of matter or the birth of the universe? Probably it's because solutions require mastery of several disciplines (at a minimum, linguistics, neurology, paleoanthropology and evolutionary biology) and in an age of specialists such expertise is rare.

In *Eve Spoke: Human Language and Human Evolution*, Philip Lieberman, a professor of cognitive science and linguistics at Brown University, tries to remedy this situation. Lieberman, who has written extensively on the evolution of the human vocal tract, seeks to bring his work to a more general audience and to integrate it with material from other fields. The catchy title underlines his support for the "out of Africa" theory of our origins. Indeed, he deserves credit for having realized, even before genetic evidence was available, that Neanderthals could hardly be our direct ancestors.

On some issues his conclusions are equally well founded. Language cannot have grown straightforwardly out of primate communication, but neither—despite its apparent uniqueness—can it have sprung up as a complete novelty. Some previously existing faculty must have been co-opted and modified. But which one was it, and how was the trick done? Obviously not by creating a self-contained "language organ." Lieberman shows how the results of new brain-imaging techniques render obsolete those models of the brain that confine language functions to the traditional Broca's and Wernicke's areas. To execute language functions, circuits must link many areas of the brain. The tough questions are, which circuits, and how do they do it?

But on the tough ones Lieberman is vague. He promises evidence new not only to general readers but to "most professional anthropologists, archeologists or linguists," yet he sticks mostly to familiar ground. He reviews phonetic studies from the 1950s and 60s, and then surveys Jane Goodall's work on chimpanzees, and early ape "language" experiments by Beatrix and Alan Gardner, as well as his own reconstruction of the Neanderthal vocal tract, the subject of two previous books. For him, the vocal tail wags the linguistic dog; he gives syntax and semantics only cursory treatment. Once our unique vocal tract developed, he claims, syntax emerged automatically from pre-existing "neural mechanisms initially adapted to regulate the precise manual motor control implicated in toolmaking," which "could have provided the initial basis for the regulation of speech motor activity."

Maybe. But how? Anyone familiar with the "motor homunculus" chart featured in introductory neurology texts knows that motor functions of hands and vocal organs are controlled from different regions of the brain, so the neural circuits involved cannot be identical. But if those regions enjoy privileged connections, what are they, how did they evolve and how do they work? Lieberman offers no answers. Indeed, he leaves himself far too little space to deal adequately with the myriad issues language evolution raises. Out of a mere 149 pages of actual text, more than 50 are devoted to the vocal tract, and almost another 30 to chimpanzees, leaving less than half the book for everything else. Even in that part, few relevant matters are discussed. For instance, there is nothing on selective pressures favoring language, or the genetic variation on which such pressures could have worked—issues that any evolutionary biologist would expect a book with Lieberman's subtitle to address.

Instead, Lieberman describes an experiment in which he and colleagues made audio recordings of climbers 24,000 feet up on Mount Everest. Unsurprisingly, both speech and the comprehension of sentences were slowed and disorganized, allegedly demonstrating that neural circuits for speech and syntax are partly shared. But since there's no way to utter sentences without sounds, it would be amazing if the circuits weren't partly shared; their current status says very little about how they evolved.

Another red herring Lieberman pursues is an attempt to refute Noam Chomsky's linguistic theories. He says "the number of putative rules" in Chomskyan linguistics "begins to approach the number of sentences. The rules of grammar become torturously complex and ultimately fail." That was true of generative grammars in the early 70s. If Lieberman had read or understood any later work, he would know that syntacticians were well aware of these problems and were dealing with them. By 1980, universal grammar was reduced to one rule and a dozen or so principles; since then it has shrunk further.

Lieberman's understanding even of pre-Chomskyan syntax seems limited. He states that correct responses by the pygmy chimpanzee Kanzi to commands like "put the ball on the pine needles" versus "put the pine needles on the ball" show that "he had mastered the canonical form of English in which the subject comes before the object." Unfortunately, these commands don't contain any subjects; they show objects preceding prepositional phrases of place.

But worse than such lapses are the tone and tactics Lieberman adopts toward anyone he disagrees with. He dismisses four decades of work by hundreds of syntacticians as "toy linguistics." He categorizes the conclusions of the psychologist and primate researcher Herbert Terrace as "absurd." He suggests without any foundation that the psycholinguist Steven Pinker believes that "sexual activity at the appropriate time of the month always results in the production of progeny."

During the last decade, several conferences, a dozen books and many articles have dealt with language evolution. Lieberman discusses hardly any of these. He implicitly portrays himself as a lone pioneer, singlehandedly garnering data from virgin fields. But for any multidisciplinary enterprise to make progress, its researchers must share a spirit of collegiality. The absence of that spirit is perhaps the gravest flaw in a book that, despite initial promise, leaves the reader frustrated and disappointed.

Sunday, May 17, 1998

Origin of Speech

By Philip Lieberman

To the Editor:

Predictably, Derek Bickerton's review (March 1) castigates my most recent book, *Eve Spoke: Human Language and Human Evolution*. Bickerton's own work follows in the footsteps of Noam Chomsky, whereas my book disputes the central premises of Chomsky's linguistic theories.

The focus of my book is the nature and evolution of the human brain's capacity for language and thought. *Eve Spoke* shows that the brain mechanisms that regulate human speech (or that can be used to produce manual sign language) form part of a complex system that also allows us to understand the syntax and meaning of sentences that we hear or read. The 19th-century theory linking language to two regions of the brain, Broca's and Wernicke's areas, is wrong. Quantitative data from studies of aphasia, Parkinson's disease, the oxygen deprivation suffered by climbers on Mount Everest and other conditions show that parts of the human brain traditionally associated with motor control are implicated in comprehending language and thinking. Studies of the brains and behavior of other species provide evidence for the continuity of evolution. Hence, I propose that the brain bases of human language could have evolved from neural mechanisms initially adapted to regulate the precise manual movements implicated, for example, in toolmaking. My book presents new insights from several investigators, relating to language, on the evolution of modern human beings and the demise of the Neanderthals.

119

My book also demonstrates that our brains are not computers, "pre-loaded" with the details of syntax. The evidence for the Chomskyan "language gene" as presented by Steven Pinker is flawed, and other experimental data that Pinker and Bickerton cite to support Chomsky's theories are incomplete and seriously misleading.

The Material Basis of the Human Voice

By Verlyn Klinkenborg

There is evidence, scientists now say, that the capacity for speech arose in ancestral humans 400,000 years ago. The evidence is structural. The hole in the back of the skull, the hypoglossal canal, through which nerve fibers connect to the tongue, is larger in early and modern humans than it is in chimpanzees and australopithecines, implying a more dexterous, more articulate tongue. We humans naturally think speaking divides us from the rest of the animals. So it is good to be reminded that the root of our difference and the source of so much proud philosophizing over the past 400 millennia lies in the material structure of the body itself.

For the last few years, I have been keenly aware of the physical nature of speech. My own voice had dwindled to a croak, rising sometimes to a wheeze, because of a painless, benign obstruction on one of my vocal cords. It had the same effect as a finger wrapped around a cello string—no vibration, no amplitude, no resonance. After a couple of failed operations, I went to a new surgeon who was able, bless her heart, to remove the obstruction completely. A week of silence passed, and then I made a few tentative noises. I sounded, to myself at least, like the Great and Mighty Oz. A rumbling rose from my chest. I could feel the vibration down through my feet, as though a train were passing.

Now, once a week, I sit in an office across 57th Street from Carnegie Hall and practice using my voice while a vocal therapist listens. I am making my tongue more dexterous. I read verses of Rossetti and Shakespeare aloud, enunciating the "n's," masticating the "m's," toothing the "t's." I say "red leather, yellow leather, blue leather" and "unique New York" again and again. I make siren noises and noises that even a chimp, with its inferior hypoglossal canal, could make. On my last visit, I sang "Row, Row, Row Your Boat," inserting a breath, per instruction, between "stream" and "merrily."

That night, across the street at Carnegie Hall, the great Swedish mezzo-soprano Anne Sofie von Otter appeared on stage, dressed in gold. After the applause fell away, her accompanist played a few supplicatory notes, and Ms. von Otter began quietly to sing one of Schubert's lieder. She sang more Schubert, then Sibelius, Mahler, Bizet, and then, at the end of the evening when the audience would not let her go, she sang "Memories of You" by Eubie Blake and "Slap That Bass" by George and Ira Gershwin.

It was, I think, the first time I ever heard the human voice for itself, listened past the music and heard the material structure on which it rested—the shaping of lips, teeth, tongue, the undergirding of breath, the very physicality of the body itself, which Ms. von Otter swayed and straightened as the phrasing demanded. She was as musical when she spoke to the audience as she was when she sang to it, and when she sang Gershwin—"Zoom, zoom, zoom. Misery you got to go"—I saw that behind the pleasure of the music there also lay the pleasure, strange as it sounds, of making noise with the mouth and lungs. As for us out there in the red plush seats, when Ms. von Otter finished, we dumbly slapped one hand against the other until our hands were sore.

5

ORIGINS OF MODERN HOMO SAPIENS

The debate over the origins of modern *Homo sapiens* and the fate of contemporaneous archaic races of the species is currently the most contentious in the field. While most experts have become polarized around one of two interpretations, the most recent evidence from genetics, as well as the fossil record, suggests a more complicated story. The debate, however, has a long intellectual history, beginning at the turn of the century and involving the problem of where to place Neanderthal in the framework of human history. Concern over the fossil record around 1900 was very Eurocentric; that is, almost all of the fossil finds at the time were dug up in European soil, with the exception of a skull, jaw and lower limb bone from Java that most experts dismissed as belonging to some species of giant gibbon. Placing the Neanderthals was, then, a critical issue that put at stake more than just the pathway of human evolution. Also woven into the debate that shredded the issues along national borders was the intricate fabric of European politics. Fossil remains that ultimately bore the name came from the Neander Valley in Germany. Not surprisingly, two ideas from German scholars placed the Neanderthals squarely in line as candidates for direct human ancestors. Point of fact, the dominant theory, proposed by the eminent anatomist Rudolf Virchow, took the position that the Neanderthals were not really different from modern humans at all but pathologically afflicted by some unknown condition that produced their brutish appearance. Mostly overwhelmed by Virchow's stature in the field, Gustav Schwalbe rather meekly proposed the possibility that Neanderthal's features were not the result of any pathology, rather this look was natural. Furthermore, these coarse-looking folk might actually be our ancestors.

The third possibility roared from the mouth of the French anatomist Marcelin Boule, who had plenty of experience dealing with Neanderthals that were dug up in sites on French soil. Boule's opinion, as one might imagine, was contrary to that of his German colleagues, but, of course, he had the added advantage of possessing other fossils that displayed steeper foreheads and more delicate anatomies, fossils so named after the equally famous French site of Cro-Magnon. While Virchow mistakenly took the characteristics of the Neanderthals to be pathological and misdiagnosed their antiquity, Boule adjudged their antiquity but failed to recognize the fact that his La Chapelle man was pathologically afflicted and reconstructed him as more ape-like than he should have been. Whatever the case, to the French the Neanderthals were so far off the direct ancestral line that they might just as well be placed in a different species, a notion Boule followed.

The title *Homo neanderthalensis* was actually bestowed by an Englishman, William King, in 1863, who had seen the original German fossil. Siding mostly with the French in their opinions of these remains, the British remained somewhat aloof from the fray, waiting for a discovery on British soil that would resolve the issue. Their time came with the announcement of the "earliest Englishman" from Piltdown.

John Noble Wilford, in "Not about Eve," his book review of Milford Wolpoff and Rachael Caspari's book *Race and Human Evolution*, presents the multiregional side of the debate. Both the genetic (mitochondrial DNA) and the fossil evidence are disputed in this book as clear evidence for alternative points of view. Wolpoff has been for years the chief spokesperson for multiregionalism and this book is a capstone of this point of view.

One good turn deserves another. If the Wolpoff and Caspari book presents the best case for multiregionalism, are we fortunate enough to have another recent book that presents the opposing point of view? We are. Robert J. Richards, a professor of history and the philosophy of science at the University of Chicago, in "Neanderthals Need Not Apply," reviews *African Exodus: The Origins of Modern Humanity* by Christopher Stringer and Robin McKie, who argue strongly for a unique African emergence of modern peoples and a subsequent spread out from Africa to other parts of the Old World. Both books are full of history that puts the debate in a proper perspective.

Just how different are the Neanderthals anyway? If we look at them from an anatomical point of view the large faces, projecting jaws, and brow ridges all distinguish them from most of modern humanity. Yet we know from other studies that rather large and obvious morphological differences can in fact be controlled by a relatively small number of genes. Genetic differences are usually much less than phenotypic ones; witness the percent difference (1–2 percent) in DNA between a chimpanzee and modern human. In "Anthropologist Links a Shift in a Skull Bone to Face of Modern Man," John Noble Wilford reports on a new anatomical study that claims that Neanderthal skull form can be rather easily changed to the modern variety with a slight shift of a single bone.

In "Strong Bones, and Thus Dim-Witted?" Tim Folger of *Discover* magazine reports on other bones of contention, this time from the postcranial skeleton. Research on the limb bones by Erik Trinkhaus and Chris Ruff suggests that in a direct contest between Neanderthals and modern humans for resources we would have out-competed the archaic version any time.

One of the most significant pieces of new evidence that confronts the issue of the origin of modern peoples unfolded with the extraction of DNA from the original Neanderthal bones by a team of German biologists. Nicholas Wade of the *New York Times*, in his article "Neanderthal DNA Sheds New Light on Human Origins," reports on this remarkable piece of work and the thoughts that some of the experts have on the meaning of the genetic differences that were discovered.

What is the message in the bit of MtDNA extracted and sequenced from the Neanderthal fossil from Neumann's valley? In "Not Our Mom," Robert Kunzig of *Discover* magazine argues that this is the critical evidence that proves the Neanderthals were a separate species from us. Christopher Stringer, paleoanthropologist at London's Natural History Museum, and Robin McKie, science editor of the *Observer*, in "Neanderthals on the Run," concur in their continuing support for an out-of-Africa model for modern human origins.

Is the message from the Neanderthal DNA as clear-cut as the proponents of the out-of-Africa model would like us to believe? Are the Neanderthals really a distinct species from ourselves? Chimpanzees and humans are different species—we can't interbreed—separated from each other by some 5 million years. On the other hand, common chimps and the bonobos are not really different species because they can interbreed. Recent genetic evidence points to their separation from a common ancestor only 1.5 million years ago. The question is, why would humans become distinct species (if they did) faster than any other primate? In "Don't Bring Politics into Neanderthal Debate; Lack of DNA Evidence," Milford Wolpoff, Alan Mann, and Rachael Caspari confront the mtDNA data that others point to as evidence that says we did.

There is no question that people throughout our history migrated from one place to another. These migrations, using the frontier model, were viewed unidirectionally. We left the homeland and settled another. Go west, young man, or east, as the case might be. Only recently have scientists considered the possibility of a condition that sooner or later affects all travelers: homesickness. In "Out of Africa and Back," Kathy Svitil of *Discover* magazine reports on genetic evidence that suggests after some migrations at least a few of us went back home.

How many people would it take to leave Africa and repopulate the Old World anyway? Genetic evidence reported on by Nicholas Wade, in

"To People the World, Start with 500," suggests that at somewhere around 140,000 years ago it could have been a lot fewer than we might think.

Do we have other evidence for an out-of-Africa migration? The Old Testament reports that Moses did, but he had to part the Red Sea to do it. Interestingly, there is little evidence of any kind to support a factual basis for this exodus. If only we had footprints pointing in the right direction. While not exactly evidence for the out-of-Africa idea, we do have footprints from a site in South Africa, as Shanti Menon of *Discover* magazine describes in "Footprints from the Human Dawn."

Nero fiddled while Rome burned. Did some Neanderthal flautist play a few mournful notes as modern *Homo sapiens* invaded Europe? John Noble Wilford, in "Playing of Flute May Have Graced Neanderthal Fire," looks at some new evidence that associates for the first time a possible musical instrument with these archaic Europeans.

It has almost always been about men and what they do. But what about the women? Were they perpetually bound up in cave-making and baby-bearing? The edited volume *Woman the Gatherer* (1981) attempted a more balanced approach to the role of women and men, and since that time new clues have emerged that have shed greater light on what women did. In "New Women of the Ice Age," Heather Pringle of *Discover* magazine describes the new research of archeologist Olga Soffer and colleagues, who have uncovered remarkable evidence of weaving by looking at impressions of thread on fired pieces of clay. With this and other evidence, they have made a strong case for "Ice-Age" women playing a "host of powerful roles" in Late Pleistocene society.

Archeologist Richard Klein believes that there is a distinct difference between anatomically modern and behaviorally modern people. He feels that the remains of anatomically modern humans can be distinguished as far back as 200,000 years ago in Africa. However, their behavior, if we look at the kinds of things that they made, is virtually indistinguishable from that of contemporary Neanderthals elsewhere. He claims that innovative behaviors, reflected in the making of art objects, is much more recent, perhaps as late as 50,000 years ago in Africa. Shanti Menon, in "Art in Australia, 60,000 Years Ago," reports on evidence that goes him one better, from a continent that we might least expect to provide it.

THE NEW YORK TIMES

Sunday, February 2, 1997

Not about Eve

BY JOHN NOBLE WILFORD

For ages, confronting the ineffable mystery of their very being, people have conceived of cosmologies to satisfy a hunger to know where they came from. In modern Western societies, the search for origins has taken a scientific turn, often undermining traditional beliefs but leaving many questions unanswered. Indeed, the catechism of paleoanthropology, the study of human origins and evolution, seems in some respects to be a series of questions without firm answers. Nowhere is this provisional quality of knowledge more evident than in the current controversy over the origins of modern humans, the first people anatomically and mentally like us. The dispute centers on two fundamentally different concepts: the out-of-Africa theory versus the multiregional theory.

Simply, one theory holds that modern *Homo sapiens* is a relatively young species that evolved in one place, Africa. This population then expanded through the world, replacing related species. The other theory posits multiple origins for the human species at different places. Archaic populations originating in Africa migrated to distant regions and there evolved into modern humans separately, though not in total genetic isolation. In this theory lies an explanation for human biological diversity as reflected in what are known as the different races.

Recent research in molecular biology—finding DNA evidence that the Eve of modern humanity seems to have lived in Africa 100,000 to 200,000 years ago—lends support to the out-of-Africa hypothesis. But fossils can yield contradictory interpretations. So scientists of equal accomplishment take opposite sides, while others hope some new discovery will resolve the issue.

The authors of *Race and Human Evolution* are ardent multiregionalists, and their book is the first comprehensive exposition of that theory for a general audience. Its publication comes none too soon, for multiregionalism has been reduced to the role of foil to the evocative Eve in most popular writing and scientific forums. A recent article in an archeology journal even called the out-of-Africa theory "effectively the only game in town."

Milford Wolpoff, a professor of anthropology at the University of Michigan, is an architect (with Alan Thorne of Australia and Wu Xinzhi of China) of the multiregional concept of human origins, and its most provocative defender. His co-author, Rachel Caspari, is a researcher in anthropology at Michigan, and his wife. Their collaboration has produced a spirited book, at times personal and combative, always earnest and thorough. They leave no doubt where they stand: "We predict we will never find a cradle of modern humanity, because a single source for modern humans does not exist."

One comes away from the book with many insights into the dynamics of developing, elaborating and defending a scientific thesis—even the frustration overtaking the authors as they saw multiregionalism being either ignored or misunderstood and thus losing the public battle. "Eve was glamorous and sexy," they concede. "Eve was a simple theory that made science reporting easy and fun. Eve gave answers and represented 20th-century technology providing answers—telling us about our origins. Eve implied the brotherhood of all humankind and was politically correct." So, as the "Eve theorists claimed the high moral ground," the authors write, multiregionalists were left behind trying to explain a more complex concept and defend it against possible misinterpretation as another example of racist thinking. It was then that they realized "how thoroughly we had inadvertently grasped the tar baby of racial politics."

Mr. Wolpoff and Ms. Caspari go to great lengths—almost half of the book—to distinguish their theory from the pre-Darwinian concept of polygenism, which at various times served as an intellectual justification for colonialism, slavery and Nazism's master race. Polygenism postulated the separate origins and independent evolution of the races along different, isolated lines. Among its influential exponents were the German scientist Ernst Haeckel in the 19th century, the Harvard anthropologist Earnest Hooton in the early 20th century and, most recently, Carleton Coon, the Harvard-trained author of *The Origin of Races*, published in 1962.

Polygenism is not to be confused with polycentrism, which the authors call "the intellectual precursor" of multiregionalism. In his work with early human fossils from China and Java in the 1930s, Franz Weidenreich, a refugee from Nazi Germany, came to the central realization of polycentrism: Races reflect regional variations but are not the product of totally isolated, parallel evolutions, for regional populations never stopped exchanging genes. The chapters of historical background, replete with fascinating accounts of past wars in anthropology, are a book within a book. One sympathizes with the authors conscientious effort to put distance between their theory and anthropology's racist past, but wishes there had been more streamlining here.

The authors seek to rebut the DNA evidence for a recent origin only in Africa, stressing flaws in data analysis cited by other scientists. They also deal with the seeming paradox at the heart of polycentrism-multiregionalism: How did populations retain regional distinctions and yet evolve together as one species, modern *Homo sapiens*? Gene flow is the answer. Fossils preserve early traces of regional variations and what is interpreted as a gradual evolution toward modern humans. But a certain amount of gene exchange insured that human evolution followed a common pattern and kept the variations from leading to separate regional species.

One source of misunderstanding about the theory, the authors believe, is its characterization as parallel evolution from a single common base long ago. Instead, they think of races "as dynamic, changing entities with temporal depth because they are not the diverging branches on an evolutionary bush but the constantly separating and merging channels in a stream."

How close does this book take us to satisfying answers to the questions of how, when and where modern humans emerged? Supporters of the out-of-Africa theory are not likely to be swayed by the arguments here, but they are put on notice that the debate is far from over.

Neanderthals Need Not Apply

By ROBERT J. RICHARDS

Do human beings constitute one species, with the several races merely regional varieties? Or are the differences among the races more profound, such that they form independent though related species, like wolves, dogs and foxes? These were questions for the 19th century, and the answers given polarized the British scientific community.

In 1864, Alfred Russel Wallace, co-author of the theory of evolution, proposed to an audience at the Anthropological Society of London that our apelike ancestors spread throughout the world and became adapted to their various local conditions. He argued that such evolution would have produced the characteristic physical traits of the races, but not immediately those mental and moral qualities that were thought typically human; the further evolution of these hominids into *Homo sapiens* would have occurred only after their social interactions had given a naturally selective advantage to linguistic, intellectual and ethical development. The question of the unity of the human species became for Wallace a matter of choice: The fixation of different anatomical types at the advent of human mind allowed us to speak of many species of man; but if we preferred to regard as the spokesman of humanity that original, undifferentiated progenitor whose mind was still brutish, then we might also declare the species to be one, but displaying many varieties.

Charles Darwin generally endorsed Wallace's thesis, though he thought sexual selection the most powerful agent in forming the races. Cleopatra's

nose, then, was not merely a chance structure, but the result of mate selection by hundreds of generations of males with Antony's predilection.
Darwin suspected that our ancestors probably evolved in Africa, since the
continent was still populated by the apes that seemed to be our collateral
relatives. For Darwin, even more than for Wallace, the question of the unity
of the human species was arbitrary, since he considered the very category
of species as simply one of convenience, marking out those individuals that
looked more or less alike. If we decided to regard the races as varieties of
one species, that would not imply they all enjoyed the same intellectual
and moral qualities. Comparative skull sizes showed, Darwin believed, the
evolutionarily advanced state of Europeans. In his travels to South America, he encountered noble Indians who often seemed morally superior to the
gauchos slaughtering them. But of the Indians of Tierra del Fuego he
thought that "if the world was searched, no lower grade of man could be
found." Notoriously, in *The Descent of Man*, he suggested the Irish might be
an exception.

At the turn of the century, the evolutionary evaluation of the races
gained depth, both from paleontological evidence and cultural presumption.
Ernst Haeckel, Darwin's German champion, celebrated the discovery in Java,
by his protege Eugene Dubois, of the "missing link," the fossil remains of
what later became known as *Homo erectus*. For Haeckel this indicated the
East Indies as the home of the "ape-man," whence this transitional creature, he supposed, spread to other locations and continued to evolve into the
several races. Haeckel, not surprisingly, thought the leading edge of human
evolution was found in the Europeans, with the Bushmen and Australians
hardly more advanced than their ape forebears. He initially regarded the
Japanese as a race of middling development—until the Russo-Japanese war,
after which he had to accelerate their evolution into second place.

The discovery of many more hominid fossils during the first half of our
century did not appreciably change the direction taken by evolutionary speculation about race in the previous century. In 1962, Carleton Coon published *The Origin of Races*, which argued that *Homo erectus* migrated out of
Africa and, in five locations throughout the world, evolved into *Homo sapiens*, but at different rates. Europeans and Asians left the other races still
clinging to more primitive physical, intellectual and cultural traits. The distinguished geneticist Theodosius Dobzhansky charged Coon with advanc-
ing ideas quite congenial to racists and white supremacists. The authors of
African Exodus take up Dobzhansky's cause.

Christopher Stringer, a paleontologist at the Natural History Museum
in London, with the help of Robin McKie, a science writer, argues for a theory that has come to be called "out of Africa"; and he opposes it to the contemporary "multiregionalist" view, a descendant of the ideas of Wallace,
Haeckel and Coon. Stringer, along with an array of other paleontologists
and geneticists, maintains that *Homo erectus*—a bipedal hominid with a brain

size roughly between that of a chimpanzee and a modern human—came out of Africa, beginning about a million years ago, and spread to the Middle and Far East. In Europe, the descendants of these protohumans evolved into Neanderthals, hominids having a brain even larger than modern humans, but apparently with only the rudiments of culture and speech. The last group of *Homo erectus* disappeared about 100,000 years ago, though Neanderthals lingered for another 70,000 years. About this much, the disputing parties agree. Those of the multiregionalist persuasion contend that the Neanderthals transmuted into modern man, at least in Europe, and that colonies of *Homo erectus* evolved within their geographical locations into *Homo sapiens*. Gene flow among the human groups, due to occasional matings at the boundaries, would have kept them all moving more or less toward sapience. Thus, over long periods of time, the different human populations—Eskimos, Pygmies, Australian Aborigines, Europeans and others—slowly became modern humans, but in distinctive ways.

The out-of-Africa theorists argue that the far-flung groups of *Homo erectus* did not evolve into the modern races, but simply went extinct in various regions of the world, except in Africa. The Neanderthals, too, eventually succumbed, about 30,000 years ago. In Africa, however, the evolutionary pot kept brewing, according to Stringer. There, about 200,000 years ago, *Homo erectus* began evolving into "late archaic *sapiens*." In another hundred millenniums this group achieved a near-modern form. And out of Africa they came, as the final colonizing wave of hominids, our ancestors. Since so little time has passed since they decamped from Africa, dispersing to the far regions of the world—100,000 years being a mere paleontological moment—"only slight differences, if any, in intellect and innate behavior are likely to have evolved between modern human populations." We are "all Africans under our skin."

Stringer marshals considerable paleontological, anthropological and genetic evidence for his position—for instance, the genetic differences within each race are much larger than the average differences among the races, suggesting very close biological relationship. The interlocking patterns of the different kinds of evidence that he dexterously deploys also give powerful support to the theory, if not the complete support his intermittent exultations would indicate. There is, for example, fair evidence, which Stringer himself mentions, that interbreeding occurred between Neanderthals and Cro-Magnons (more recent *Homo sapiens*), which would argue a virtuous intermediate position.

The repulsive force separating the out-of-Africa theory from the multiregional theory seems generated as much by the contemporary personalities involved in the debate as by the ancient evidence debated. The out-of-Africa theory does have the advantage of supporting our better inclinations, which the authors thoroughly engage by casting the opposition as inheritors of a culturally infected biology. Stringer recounts his encounter in 1979, in a men's washroom at Harvard, with the aged Coon, who referred to one of his critics as "that … Jew Weiner." He represents more recent opponents, like Loring Brace and Milford Wolpoff of the University of Michigan, as decidedly less obvious in their attitudes, though still indelibly tinctured, with Brace issuing "vicious" attacks and Wolpoff curtly "dismissive" of Stringer's methods. One suspects that for this popular exposition, the journalist partner of this duo encouraged his co-author to put a human face on science. Ironically, that face does reveal, in the firelight of controversy, vestiges of an ancient ancestry.

THE NEW YORK TIMES

Tuesday, May 19, 1998

Anthropologist Links a Shift
in a Skull Bone to Face of Modern Man

By JOHN NOBLE WILFORD

One look at the face of a human being and the skull of a Neanderthal is enough to see a striking difference. The Neanderthal face projects out from the cranium. The human's is aligned more vertically, directly below the cranium. In fact, humans are unique among mammals in their lack of forward projecting faces.

An anthropologist at Rutgers University thinks he has found the most likely anatomical basis for this distinctive facial characteristic. He has determined that the shape and dimensions of the anatomically modern human head and face depend to a large extent on the size and changes over time of one pivotal bone, the sphenoid.

In a close examination of the sphenoid in humans and their archaic hominid relatives, Dr. Daniel E. Lieberman of Rutgers found the bone to be a kind of cornerstone of the skull. Lying at the base of the brain case, behind the palate and in front of the vertebral column and as wide as the skull, the sphenoid joins 17 of the 22 bones in the skull. The face, in a sense, grows forward from the sphenoid.

Comparing modern and archaic skulls, Dr. Lieberman noted that the length of the human sphenoid is 20 to 30 percent shorter than the similar bone in other hominids, including Neanderthals. The longer sphenoid bone had presumably been the major factor dictating the long projecting faces of Neanderthals, which became extinct in Europe 30,000 years ago, and archaic species like *Homo heidelbergensis,* considered by some paleontologists to be the immediate direct predecessor of modern *Homo sapiens.*

"So just change the shape of one bone and it has all kinds of effects on how much the face projects in front of the brain case," Dr. Lieberman said. "In turn, facial projection affects all sorts of aspects of our overall cranial shape, such as how large our brow ridge is and how steep our forehead is."

The reduction of facial projection, the anthropologist said, contributes to the more globular shape of modern human craniums, compared with the flat, sloping brain cases of Neanderthals. His investigations were based on X-ray pictures and computed tomography scans of human and early hominid skulls. One difficulty was the scarcity of sphenoid bones, which are fragile and often are not preserved in skull fossils.

From this perspective at least, Dr. Lieberman said in an interview, "it doesn't seem to take a lot to turn a Neanderthal into a human."

The shortening of the sphenoid presumably occurred about 125,000 year ago. That was about when anatomically modern humans first appeared in Africa and later drove archaic relatives to extinction.

Dr. Lieberman was cautious about possible implications of the findings for the rise of humans or the fall of Neanderthals. Perhaps the changing shape of the face led to adjustments in the placement of the larynx, which might account for the development of more articulate speech in modern humans, compared with that of the Neanderthals. That is only speculation, he emphasized.

Neanderthal speech, like most aspects about these Ice Age hunters, is controversial. Recent evidence by Duke University anthropologists indicated that Neanderthals and other hominids as far back as 400,000 years ago may have been able to speak, though other scientists continue to believe this ability was limited until modern *Homo sapiens* came along.

In a report of the findings in [an] issue of the journal *Nature,* Dr. Lieberman concluded, "Sphenoid reduction, through its effects on facial projection and cranial shape, may account for the apparently rapid evolution of modern human cranial form, and suggests that Neanderthals and other archaic *Homo* should be excluded from *H. sapiens.*"

This analysis, scientists said, supports recent human evolution research indicating that modern humans arose in Africa and then spread through the world, instead of evolving in different parts of the world from archaic species there. If the new findings are correct, modern humans would appear to be more closely related to each other than they are to the archaic *Homo* species that preceded them in various regions of Europe and Asia.

Dr. Fred H. Smith, a paleoanthropologist at Northern Illinois University in DeKalb, who specializes in studies of Neanderthals and other archaic hominids, said the sphenoid hypothesis "makes a lot of sense."

If anything, the faces of modern humans are getting smaller with time.

The earliest members of the modern species had huge faces that were especially long from front to back. Since the end of the most recent Ice Age, about 12,000 years ago, the evolutionary trend has been to smaller faces, presumably because changes in diet reduced the need for robust chewing muscles and jaws.

Strong Bones, and Thus Dim-Witted?

By Tim Folger

Why did Neanderthals disappear some 30,000 years ago, while *Home sapiens* continues to thrive?... [A]nthropologists Erik Trinkaus and Chris Ruff ... [believe] they [have] found some clues: The Neanderthals had stronger arms and they ran their children ragged.

The two anthropologists studied about two dozen fossil skeletons of Neanderthals and early modern humans, all from well-excavated sites in the Near East—the oldest dating from 150,000 years ago—where both populations lived at various times. Although anthropologists aren't sure whether the two peoples ever overlapped, they clearly had much in common, says Trinkaus, who works at the University of New Mexico. "In the Near East both humans and Neanderthals are found with archeological material that is, except in subtle details, indistinguishable," he says. "They made the same type of tools, they hunted the same type of animals, they lived in very similar places."

Why then did one group vanish and the other prosper? The answer, says Trinkaus, may be found in their bones. He and Ruff, who teaches at Johns Hopkins, used X-rays and computer models of the fossils to study the stresses the bones were subjected to during life. They found that Neanderthal bones consistently seem to reflect more vigorous activity. The most likely explanation, says Trinkaus, given that both populations used essential the same tools in the same environment, is that Neanderthals used their tools less efficiently. The extra effort put additional loads on the bones, which, as weight lifters know, strengthens them.

Using a computer program designed for orthopedic research, Ruff and Trinkaus measured the cross-sectional structure of the bones, a basic indicator of strength. They then factored in the Neanderthals' and humans' different proportions, to allow for the former's greater weight and overall robustness. Finally they compared the relative strength of arm and leg bones from the two groups.

The strength of the leg bones of Neanderthals and early modern humans turned out to be equal. But the upper arm bones of Neanderthals were significantly stronger than those in humans. This means, Trinkaus thinks, that humans probably chose food that was easier to process or they used their tools more intelligently and less laboriously. One of the keys to evolutionary success, says Trinkaus, is the efficient use of energy. The more efficient a people, the better their chances of surviving. "It takes only a very subtle difference in life-style to make a big difference in terms of evolutionary success," he says.

This work complemented earlier research by Trinkaus on differences in Neanderthal and human hipbones, particularly in the knobby neck of the femur, or thighbone, which fits into the hip socket. Modern studies have shown that this neck tends to get bent in active children. In Neanderthal, Trinkaus found, it was much more sharply bent than it was in humans. He interprets this to mean that Neanderthal children had to accompany adults on foraging trips, while human children remained at camp with other adults. Such a social structure may have given early human children a better chance of survival.

Critics say Ruff and Trinkaus may not be justified in inferring so much about behavior from skeletons. But Trinkaus says his work fits other evidence that early humans simply outcompeted Neanderthals for resources. "We can say from the fossils that these populations were using their bodies in very different ways to manipulate their environment."

Friday, July 11, 1997

Neanderthal DNA Sheds New Light on Human Origins

BY NICHOLAS WADE

A hauntingly brief but significant message extracted from the bones of a Neanderthal who lived at least 30,000 years ago has cast new light both on the origin of humans and Neanderthals and on the long disputed relationship between the two.

The message consists of a short strip of the genetic material DNA that has been retrieved and deciphered despite the age of the specimen. It indicates that Neanderthals did not interbreed with the modern humans who started to supplant them from their ancient homes about 50,000 years ago.

The message also suggests, said the biologists who analyzed it, that the Neanderthal lineage is four times older than the human lineage, meaning that Neanderthals split off much earlier from the hominid line than did humans.

The finding, made by a team of scientists led by Dr. Svante Pääbo of the University of Munich in Germany, marks the first time that decodable DNA has been extracted from Neanderthal remains and is the oldest hominid DNA so far retrieved. The DNA was extracted from the original specimen of Neanderthals, found in the Neander valley near Dusseldorf, Germany, in 1856, and is now in the Rheinisches Landesmuseum in Bonn.

"This is obviously a fantastic achievement," said Dr. Chris Stringer, an expert on Neanderthals at the Museum of Natural History in London.

Many anthropologists had tried to extract DNA from Neanderthal bones without success. "Clearly, it's a coup," Dr. Maryellen Ruvolo, an anthropologist at Harvard University, said of the Munich team.

The Neanderthals were large, thick-boned individuals with heavy brows and a brain case as large as that of modern humans but stacked behind the face instead of on top of it. They lived in Europe and western Asia from 300,000 years ago, dying out about 270,000 years later.

For the latter part of that period they clearly coexisted with modern humans but the relationship between the two groups, whether fraternal or genocidal, has been debated ever since the first Neanderthal was discovered. Early humans and Neanderthals may have interbred, as some scientists contend, with modern Europeans being descended from both; or the two hominid lines may have remained distinct, with humans displacing and probably slaughtering their rivals.

The new finding, reported in [an] issue of the journal *Cell*, comes down firmly on the side of Neanderthals having been a distinct species that contributed nothing to the modern human gene pool. Calling it "an incredible breakthrough in studies of human evolution," Dr. Stringer said the results showed Neanderthals "diverged away from our line quite early on, and this reinforces the idea that they are a separate species from modern humans."

Dr. Ian Tattersall, a paleontologist at the American Museum of Natural History in Manhattan, said the finding "fits well into my view of the fossil record," although there was still a "very tenacious notion of Neanderthals having given rise to *Homo sapiens* or interbred with them."

The new work was also praised by scientists who study ancient DNA, a lively new field, which has included reports of DNA millions of years old being retrieved from dinosaur bones, fossil magnolia leaves and insects entombed in amber. Although these reports have appeared in leading scientific journals like *Science* and *Nature*, other scientists have been unable to reproduce them. In at least one case the supposed fossil DNA was contaminated by contemporary human DNA.

But a leading critic of these claims of ancient DNA extraction, Tomas Lindahl of the Imperial Cancer Research Fund in England, has given the new work his seal of approval, calling it "arguably the greatest achievement so far in the field of ancient DNA research."

The Munich team took great pains to verify that it had a genuine sample of Neanderthal DNA. Working in sterile conditions, team members isolated it in two different laboratories and distinguished it from the human DNA, which contaminated the bones. Their work is "compelling and convincing," Dr. Lindahl wrote in a commentary in *Cell*.

The DNA recovered from the Neanderthal is known as mitochondrial DNA, a type especially useful for monitoring human evolution. Mitochondria are tiny, bacteria-like organelles within the cell and possess their own DNA. They exist in eggs, but not in sperm, and so are passed down through the female line. Unlike the main human genes on the chromosomes, which get shuffled each generation, the only change to mitochondrial DNA is the accidental change caused by copying errors, radiation or other mishaps.

Once a change, or mutation, becomes established in mitochondrial DNA, it gets passed on to all of that woman's descendants. Tracking mutations is a powerful way of constructing family trees. The branch points on such a family tree can also be dated with some plausibility if at least one of them can be matched to a known event in the fossil record, like the parting of the human and chimpanzee lines.

The Munich team focused on a particularly variable region of mitochondrial DNA and reconstructed the Neanderthal version of it, 378 units in length. Comparing it with modern human DNA from five continents, they found it differed almost equally from all of them, signaling no special relationship with contemporary Europeans, as would have been expected if Neanderthals and modern humans interbred.

In addition, the family tree of Neanderthal mutations, when compared with those of the chimpanzee and human, yielded a distinctive pattern of variations. In the authors' interpretation, Neanderthals branched off the hominid line first, followed by humans much later.

According to the fossil and archeological record, humans and Neanderthals diverged at least 300,000 years ago. The mitochondrial DNA evidence agrees well with this date, the authors say, since individual genes would be expected to diverge before the divergence of populations.

From fossil evidence the human and chimpanzee lines are thought to have diverged some 4 million to 5 million years ago, a date that helps anchor the tree drawn from the new genetic data. The split between Neanderthal and human mitochondrial DNA, which marks the start of the split between the human and Neanderthal lineages, would have occurred between 550,000 and 690,000 years ago, the authors say, while the individual from whom all modern human mitochondrial DNA is descended would have lived 120,000 to 150,000 years ago.

Acknowledging the uncertainty in these dates, the authors say they show at least that Neanderthal lineage is four times as old as the human lineage, as measured by mitochondrial DNA.

The Munich team's report ranges over the three treacherous fields of paleoanthropology, ancient DNA and the genetics of human evolution. Dr. Svante Pääbo has criticized many claims of ancient DNA and sought to lay out his methods with care. That was part of the reason for choosing to publish his work in *Cell*, which specializes in rigorous molecular biology, rather than more widely read journals like *Science* and *Nature*.

Dr. Mark Stoneking of Pennsylvania State University, an expert on human evolution and a member of the Munich team, said *Cell* offered more space to describe the team's methods. Also, Dr. Stoneking said, "this was in the background of Svante despairing over some of the claims of ancient DNA published in *Science* and *Nature*."

The interpretation of the Neanderthal mitochondrial data may be open to debate on the dating.

"Deriving these dates involves making a lot of supposition about the neutrality of the mitochondrial genome and the speed of accretion of new changes," Dr. Tattersall said.

But Dr. Ruvolo said the Munich team's methods seemed sound and its interpretation of the data was likely to be accepted. "There could be minor quibbles over the dates but the overall properties of the tree won't change," she said.

DISCOVER

January 1998

Not Our Mom

By Robert Kunzig

A small stretch of DNA from a Neanderthal bone was described this past year, and it doesn't look like ours. The bone was the right humerus, or upper-arm bone, of the Neander Valley skeleton itself, discovered near Düsseldorf in 1856; the DNA was from the "control region" of mitochondrial DNA. The control region codes for nothing, and so natural selection ignores it; and sex does too, because unlike the DNA that makes us visibly who we are, the stuff in the cell nucleus, mitochondrial DNA is passed intact from mother—and only from mother—to child. In theory, the control region comes to each one of us out of the deep past, like a taste for chicken soup, via an endless bucket brigade of mothers, altered only by random mutations. If some of us had a Neanderthal in that maternal line, her imprint ought to be discernible. Svante Pääbo of the University of Munich and his colleagues looked at the DNA from their single Neanderthal, and they looked at DNA from more than 1,600 modern Europeans, Africans, Asians, native Americans and Australians, and Oceanians. They saw no evidence of a relation.

The work was widely hailed as a technical triumph—reassuring in a year when earlier reports of far more ancient DNA from insects in amber seemed to be crumbling. Few labs besides Pääbo's, it seems clear, would have been able to extract the Neanderthal DNA from liquefied bone samples that contained only some 50 copies of the target molecule. A graduate student named Matthias Krings did the hard work—amplifying the scarce DNA by means of the polymerase chain reaction, cloning it, and finally determining its sequence. "It was Krings who put in the 100-hour weeks," says Ralf Schmitz of the Rheinisches Amt für Bodendenkmalpflege, an agency responsible for archeology in the Rhineland. "When he saw there might be something in there, he just kept working until he was sure."

But it was Schmitz, a young archeologist, who made the project happen in the first place. In 1991 the Rheinisches Landesmuseum in Bonn authorized him to organize new studies of its prize fossil. Schmitz got in touch with Pääbo, who had extracted DNA from a 30,000-year-old horse buried in permafrost. At first Pääbo was discouraging: The chances of getting DNA out of a Neanderthal that was anywhere from 30,000 to 100,000 years old and that had not been frozen, he said, were very slim—too slim to convince the custodians of the fossil. "It's as if you're cutting a piece out of the Mona Lisa to study the paint," says Schmitz. "You have to have good arguments for doing that."

By 1996, though, gene-extraction techniques had improved, Pääbo was willing, and Schmitz got permission. In June of that year, he and Heike Krainitzki, a professional bone preparator, entered the steel vault where the bones are stored in a steel box in a steel cabinet—the Landesmuseum keeps only the skullcap with the famous browridges on display. "The nervous tension was enormous," Schmitz recalls. "We were both very tense. Krainitzki didn't want anyone else to be there. A German TV network had wanted to broadcast it live, but she wouldn't do it." The two of them wore protective clothing and surgeons' masks to avoid contaminating the bone. With a goldsmith's saw Krainitzki cut a half-inch thick, eighth-of-an-ounce, half-moon slice from the right humerus—the bone that X-rays and other tests had shown was best preserved. She and Schmitz then immediately carried the slice to Munich. There Krings drilled tiny samples from the cortex; the hard calcium carbonate in that outer layer offers DNA more protection against the outside world than it gets in the marrow.

Five months later Schmitz was back in Munich.... Krings had extracted a bit of DNA that he thought was Neanderthal. He was now repeating the whole experiment with a separate hundredth-of-an-ounce bit of bone drilled from that half-moon slice. If he got the same DNA sequence again, he would be virtually certain he was not looking at a modern human contaminant. The results, Schmitz remembers, came in one November evening at 10:14 P.M. "It felt as if we had climbed Everest," he says. Later there would be another occasion for celebration: The results were confirmed by an independent laboratory, that of Mark Stoneking at Penn State, which got the same sequence from another bit of the Neanderthal bone.

Careful controls like that seem to have convinced the researchers' peers, after the paper was published last July, that Krings and his colleagues did indeed have the first bit of Neanderthal DNA and the oldest bit of DNA ever extracted from a human being. What sort of human the Neanderthal was, however, remains subject to debate. There are two main schools of thought.

One holds that Neanderthals are our ancestors, or rather are ancestors primarily of modern Europeans; in this view modern humans evolved from archaic ones such as Neanderthals in different parts of the world simultaneously, all the while exchanging enough genes to remain part of the same species. The other view is that Neanderthals were a separate species that were replaced, after little or no fraternization, by modern humans, who began migrating out of Africa around 100,000 years ago.

The Neanderthal DNA does not resolve the issue—but it suggests Neanderthals were indeed a separate species, and thus it favors the out-of-Africa hypothesis. Krings's 379-nucleotide sequence differed at 27 positions, on average, from the modern human sequences, and it was no closer to Europeans than to any other moderns. Among themselves the modern sequences differed by an average of only eight places. Picture a crowd of modern humans huddled around a campfire, with nobody more than eight yards from the center; then the Neanderthal is 27 yards away, well outside the circle, in the shadows at the edge of the woods. By Pääbo's and Krings's calculations, *Homo sapiens* and *Homo neanderthalensis* must have evolved separately for more than half a million years to have become so different.

Of course, the researchers have only looked at one bit of DNA from one Neanderthal. Only when they or others have compared it with DNA from a second Neanderthal will the Munich result be fully convincing. It is fitting, though, that the first Neanderthal DNA came from the first Neanderthal—and even from one of the bones that stayed the shovels of the miners in 1856, after they had already unwittingly tossed the skullcap and other bones out of Little Feldhofer Cave, down into the valley of the Düssel River. There is no Neander River, you see; the valley got its name in the late seventeenth century from a preacher and poet who often went there, a man named Joachim Neumann. In English his name would be Newman, but in the fashion of his day Neumann translated it into Greek, and it became Neander. A century and a half later, by a remarkable coincidence, the New Man Valley yielded a truly new man—a separate species of human, it now seems. It is wonderful, really, that after another century and a half, the Neanderthal Man himself should once again be in the news.

Neanderthals on the Run

By CHRISTOPHER STRINGER AND ROBIN McKIE

They were big, brawny and, despite the bad publicity, fairly brainy as well. But the role and fate of Europe's most famous cavemen, the Neanderthals, have puzzled scientists for decades.

Were these ancient folks the ancestors of all people of European origin living today? Or were they only evolutionary cousins, a different species destined to die out 30,000 years ago in caves in France and Spain?

For years, those who held the former view dominated academe, but in the last decade they have been forced to concede ground, often acrimoniously, to the latter theory: that Neanderthals, despite modern, humanlike behavior—care of their injured and burial of their dead, for example—were not our ancestors.

Skull shapes, measurements of leg and arm bones, and the dating of fossil finds all indicate that Europeans did not evolve from Neanderthals, but from the people who replaced the Neanderthals. And recent work led by Dr. Svante Pääbo at Munich University may have ended the debate.

Dr. Pääbo's team has extracted and cloned Neanderthal DNA and shown that it is markedly different from ours, and certainly not the DNA of a species that is supposed to be an immediate forebear of *Homo sapiens*. We can now say from their genes that the Neanderthal line began to separate from ours more than a half million years ago.

But whose genes do we possess? If they are not from Neanderthal, what is their origin? These are questions that have been largely ignored in the wake of Dr. Pääbo's exciting work. Yet the answers are important, for they tell us much about our own nature and identity: that we all have a recent African origin.

The people who replaced the Neanderthals 40 millennia ago, the Cro-Magnons, began to emerge from Africa less than 100,000 years ago. The African emigrants eventually replaced all other hominid species—Neanderthals in Europe, Solo Man in Java and the descendants of Peking Man in China.

The implications for the idea of race are profound. If modern humanity is made up of people who are all recent descendants of a few African pioneers, it is equally clear that *Homo sapiens* must be a startlingly homogenous species. We simply have not had time to diverge genetically in any meaningful manner.

And that, indeed, is the case. If we compare ourselves with our nearest evolutionary cousin, the common chimpanzee of Central Africa, we find it has three subspecies, "races" that—using a genetic analysis—are almost 10 times as different from each other as are the African, European and Asian categories of *Homo sapiens*.

In the past, the races were assumed to be the vestiges of million-year-old cleavages in the human family tree. Race had a profound biological meaning by that reckoning. But now it has become apparent that our differentiation into Eskimos, Bushmen, Australians, Scandinavians and so on occurred only in the last 50,000 years, and that race is a short and superficial coda to the long song of evolution.

Nevertheless, some scientists and those with narrow political agendas have put forward arguments to sustain the idea that races exist with fundamental biological differences.

Instead of concocting divisive theories, we would be better served to recognize the importance of recent data that will help us find the attributes that separated *Homo sapiens* from other early humans like the Neanderthals. The bones and blood of the dead and the living now provide the broad outlines of how we began and then prospered.

Our DNA lineage points unmistakably to a common ancestor whose offspring evolved into *Homo sapiens* shortly before the African exodus. Though modern humans may not look exactly alike, we are indeed all Africans under the skin.

THE NEW YORK TIMES

Saturday, August 2, 1997

Don't Bring Politics into Neanderthal Debate; Lack of DNA Evidence

By Milford Wolpoff, Alan Mann, and Rachel Caspari

To the Editor:

With the analysis of a small piece of Neanderthal mitochondrial DNA, we look forward to an exciting time of competing ideas. But Chris Stringer and Robin McKie, in their July 27 Op-Ed article arguing that our DNA can be traced to a relatively recent African ancestor, stifle this process by trying to discredit their opposition and playing the race card.

Their opposition, they say, is motivated by "narrow political agendas," to "sustain the idea that races exist with fundamental biological differences." They accuse the opposition of concocting theories to back this agenda. Opposing scientists do not have political agendas. The differences live on because the new DNA results are not complete or unambiguous enough to resolve the main questions about human origins.

Nor can the new data resuscitate the writers' failed Eve theory: that if we are relatively recent descendants of African origin, we are "a startlingly homogeneous species" and haven't "had time to diverge genetically in any meaningful manner."

Only the maternally inherited mitochondrial DNA is homogeneous today. Human nuclear DNA has normal variation for a primate. What the Neanderthal DNA shows is that there was normal mitochondrial DNA variation earlier as well.

Having only a few African ancestors would have reduced nuclear and mitochondrial DNA variation, but mitochondrial DNA would recover variation faster than nuclear DNA because it mutates faster. In modern humans, however, it is the nuclear, not the mitochondrial, DNA variation that is normal. Clearly another scenario must have occurred.

DISCOVER

January 1998

Out of Africa and Back

By Kathy Svitil

The out-of-Africa theory may be in the ascendant, but it got a little more complicated this past year. Geneticist Michael Hammer of the University of Arizona in Tucson reported evidence that after the initial exodus roughly 100,000 years ago, some human ancestors in Asia may have migrated back to Africa, leaving a genetic stamp on populations there that was later carried out of Africa again on subsequent migrations.

Hammer's argument is based on his analysis of a small stretch of DNA called YAP. Located on the Y chromosome, it is the male equivalent of mitochondrial DNA—it doesn't code for a protein, and it passes from father to son altered only by a steady accumulation of random mutations. As a result, populations that have interbred recently will have more similarities in their YAP DNA than will populations that have long been separated. By looking at the differences in YAP DNA in modern populations—1,500 men from 60 populations in Europe, Asia, Africa, and Australia—Hammer was able to reconstruct a paternal family tree for the Y chromosome.

He found that the YAP DNA of some modern African men seems to have descended from much older YAP in Asian populations. "This leads us to believe that there was a significant period of evolutionary time when people in Asia evolved their own types of Y chromosomes, and then later spread that to Africa," says Hammer. After the African exodus, he thinks, early modern humans spent thousands of years living "somewhere north of the Himalayan Mountains but south of Siberia" before some returned to Africa between 50,000 and 10,000 years ago.

A sojourn in Asia is also supported by the work of population geneticist Rosalind Harding at Oxford. Harding conducted a study similar to Hammer's but looked at a different stretch of DNA from populations in Africa, Asia, Australia, Papua New Guinea, and Europe. She found evidence for a migration from Asia back to Africa more than 50,000 years ago. Instead of the simple picture of modern humans originating in Africa and then colonizing the rest of the world, she says, the new evidence presents a view of human origins that is more messy and confusing—and therefore probably more realistic. "There was a lot of diversity generated in Asia," she says, "and some of it went back to Africa."

To People the World, Start with 500

By Nicholas Wade

As few as 500 or so people, trekking out of Africa 140,000 years ago, may have populated the rest of the globe. These estimates are derived from a novel kind of archeology, one that depends not on pick and shovel but on delving into the capacious archive of the human genome.

Dates and numbers based solely on genetic evidence are unlikely to be fully accepted until historians and archeologists have had their say. But they afford a glimpse of the rich historical information embedded in the DNA of each human cell. Because of rapid methods for sequencing, or reading off, the chemical letters of DNA, geneticists are gathering reams of data about human populations. But methods of interpreting the information are still a work in progress.

At a conference on human evolution ... at the Cold Spring Harbor Laboratory on Long Island, population geneticists reported new analyses confirming that the origin of the human species is to be sought in Africa. They also discussed other inferences that can be teased out of genetic data, like estimates of the size and location of ancestral populations and the timing of the migrations out of Africa.

The geneticists' calculations depend on a number of assumptions, and tend to yield dates that have wide margins of error, a source of frustration to others at the conference. "Why should we worry about their dates?" one archeologist said to another. "It's they who should worry about our dates."

Still, a method that from a few drops of blood can reach into the dawn of human history is hard to ignore, whatever its present imperfections.

Overall, the genetic variation found among people is very small compared with that among most other species; humans evolved too recently to have accumulated any significant amount of genetic change or mutations. Still, people are far from being clones and there is a lot of variation for geneticists to track, much of which was present at the emergence of the species.

Movements of populations have been studied in the past by comparing the cell's working parts, the proteins whose structure is coded in DNA. But a coding region of DNA cannot change very much, since mutations will alter the protein it specifies, often with fatal consequences for the individual. Most of the genome, however, is composed of noncoding DNA, where mutations make no difference to the individual since most noncoding DNA has no evident purpose. Mutations in noncoding DNA are ideal for the population geneticist, since they accumulate at a fairly regular rate, yielding the best data as to the diversity and age of different populations.

One result that stands out from genetic samples of people around the world is that sub-Saharan African populations possess greater genetic diversity than non-Africans. Non-Africans retain just a subset of this diversity, as would be expected when a smaller group breaks away from a founding population, taking only a sample of the full range of genetic variation.

Dr. Mark Stoneking, a population geneticist at Pennsylvania State University, estimated at the conference that the non-Africans had split away from the main human population in Africa 137,000 years ago, give or take 15,000 years. His findings were based on sampling 34 populations around the world and analyzing genetic elements called Alu insertions, small and apparently useless pieces of DNA that have gradually spread throughout the human genome.

The substantial diversity of Alu insertions among African populations suggested that Africans maintained a larger population size through the prehistorical period than those who emigrated, Dr. Stoneking said, since small populations tend to lose their genetic diversity over time.

The original human population is thought to have numbered a few thousand individuals. Studies of mitochondrial DNA, a special category of genetic material that is inherited just through the mother's line, have put the founding human population at a mere 10,000 individuals. Using genetic markers from the chromosomes, Dr. Sarah A. Tishkoff, an evolutionary biologist at Penn State, said she and her colleagues had calculated that the long-term early population was considerably larger, from 23,000 to 447,000 individuals.

The home of the ancestral human population in Africa is not yet known but some signs point toward East Africa. The Turkana people of Kenya show the greatest diversity of any known group in their mitochondrial DNA, said Dr. Elizabeth Watson of Massey University in New Zealand.

This type of genetic material is exempt from the shuffling that creates new individuals and changes only by collecting mutations over time.

Dr. Watson said that other peoples of East Africa also had high diversity in their mitochondrial DNA, and that the region of the highest diversity was usually indicative of a species' place of origin. Since fossil remains of early human ancestors have been found at Lake Turkana in Kenya, her proposal is plausible, other experts said, although more diverse African groups may turn up after wider sampling.

Dr. Tishkoff believes that the African and non-African populations may have separated in several stages. She has found that the falashas, Ethiopian Jews who now live in Israel but are believed to be like other Ethiopians genetically, show genetic diversity intermediate between that of Africans and non-Africans, suggesting they may be descendants of a group that moved away from the main sub-Saharan population and lived perhaps in northeast Africa. Today's non-African populations could have originated from the northeast African group, carrying off even lesser genetic diversity.

There may have been more than one migration out of Africa, but if so, all probably came from northeast Africa, since the pattern of variation among non-Africans suggests that they all descend from a single ancestral gene pool, Dr. Tishkoff said.

The genetic diversity of non-Africans is so much smaller that the group leaving Africa could have consisted of as few as 200 to 500 individuals, Dr. Tishkoff and colleagues estimated, although, of course, the actual numbers may have been greater.

There seems to have been one principal migration of modern humans out of Africa, but geneticists have picked up traces of at least one earlier exodus. Dr. Stoneking believes from his Alu insertion study that peoples now found only in parts of Australasia are closely related to the ancestral human population and may have reached the far Pacific through a tropical route, to be largely displaced by a later wave of people coming through Central Asia.

A family tree of human populations can be drawn up from analysis of mitochondrial DNA, which because it accumulates mutations quite rapidly is useful for studying recent evolutionary events. The pattern of mutations in mitochondrial DNA can be traced back to an ancestral mutation pattern, whose date can be estimated by various means. Dr. Douglas C. Wallace of Emory University in Atlanta said that the age of all African mitochondrial DNAs could be set at 130,000 to 170,000 years ago, that of Asians at 50,000 to 70,000 years and the root of the European lineages at 40,000 to 50,000 years ago.

Native Americans, by the evidence of their mitochondrial DNA, fall into four genetic groups, three of which can also be found in most present-day Siberians, Dr. Wallace said.

Population geneticists have started to analyze the male or Y chromosome, which like mitochondrial DNA is a useful genetic marker because it largely escapes the reshuffling of genes in each generation. The reason is that the Y chromosome exchanges genetic information just at its tips with its counterpart, the X chromosome, leaving the main body of the Y to change only by successive random alterations in its DNA. As with mitochondrial DNA, plotting these random mutations yields a tree with the oldest mutation at the trunk and younger mutations forming successive branches.

Mitochondrial DNA and the Y chromosome should tell more or less the same story of population history unless men and women did significant travel without each other. From studying the Y chromosome of 1,500 men around the world, Dr. Michael Hammer of the University of Arizona said the family tree of present mutations started around 185,000 years ago, a date similar to that of the ancestral mitochondrial DNA.

But unlike the mitochondrial DNA tree, which mirrors the migration of people out of Africa and around the world, Y chromosome DNA shows evidence of a male migration from Asia back into Africa. This finding implies "that males dispersed more than females during these major population movements," Dr. Hammer said.

The new findings described at the conference, buttressed by the recent sequencing of mitochondrial DNA from the fossil bone of a Neanderthal, support the belief of many paleoanthropologists in the out-of-Africa theory. This is the view that modern humans emerged from Africa and displaced, without interbreeding, the archaic hominids like Neanderthals that had populated the world during earlier emigrations. Dr. Milford Wolpoff of the University of Michigan staunchly upheld his alternative view that modern humans evolved from Neanderthals in Europe and from other archaic hominids in different parts of the world. At least for the moment, however, he seems to be in an embattled minority.

Remains of anatomically modern humans have been found from as long as 200,000 years ago in Africa but some archeologists, like Dr. Richard G. Klein of Stanford University, distinguish between anatomically modern and behaviorally modern people. A suite of new artifacts, like the making of art objects, appears in the archeological record in Africa 50,000 years ago and a few thousand years later in Asia and Europe. "There was some kind of Rubicon that was crossed 40,000 to 50,000 years ago," Dr. Klein said, suggesting that the Rubicon was a neurological change that permitted the development of language.

Another archeologist, Dr. Stanley Ambrose of the University of Illinois at Urbana, agreed with Dr. Klein on the date of the change but said that language had developed much earlier. He argued that the behavioral changes seen at 50,000 years ago reflected a population recovery after an adverse climate change, particularly a deep global cold snap caused by the gigantic volcanic eruption of Mount Toba in Sumatra 73,500 years ago.

Population genetics is at its most fascinating in exploring the origin of humans, but can also be brought to bear on more recent events like the peopling of the Americas or the prehistory of populations in Asia. During an expedition across Central Asia last summer, Dr. Spencer Wells of Stanford University collected blood from speakers of 32 different languages in the region. Analyzing the DNA in his laboratory, he found that many Turkish speakers carry a harmless mutation that first arose among the Indo-Iranian peoples who lived north of the Caspian Sea some 5,000 years ago, as well as another genetic marker found among Mongoloids.

A southward migration of the Indo-Iranian speakers into India began the spread of the Indo-European languages, which include English. There must also have been an eastward migration, Dr. Wells believes, that reached the Altai Mountains north of Mongolia, and from a fusion with Mongoloid peoples of the Altai, the Turkish-speaking peoples emerged.

DISCOVER

January 1998

Footprints from the Human Dawn

By SHANTI MENON

One day after a heavy rain, a small person—a woman or a teenager—walked across a wet sand dune toward what is now Langebaan Lagoon near Cape Town, South Africa, and turned to walk east along the water's edge. The footprints that person left behind, around 117,000 years ago, are the oldest known tracks made by a modern human. Geologist David Roberts spotted the prints in late 1996 while studying the dunes. His colleague Lee Berger, a paleoanthropologist at the University of Witwatersrand in Johannesburg, announced the discovery in August.

The prints have been dated by several methods that converge on 117,000 years. "The arch, the ball of the foot, everything says these are anatomically modern human footprints," says Berger. The stride length and the depth of the prints suggest they were made by a person just over five feet tall. At one point he or she curled a big toe into the wet sand. "It's a tremendous thing to think that 117,000 years ago, a person was squishing through that wet sand just like we do today," says Berger. He admits he tried to fit his foot into one of the dainty prints—but only after putting a preservative in first. "Come on, could you resist?" he asks.

The two and a half steps, one of only three sets of human tracks in the African fossil record, were preserved when loose, dry sand blew over the wet, packed tracks, after which the underlying sand turned into rock. Berger plans to excavate more of the trackway, which is cut off by the sheer face of a dune. "I hope she tripped a few feet back so we can see her splayed out like a sand angel," he jokes.

Tools and bones from nearby sites show that the earliest modern humans originated in this area before—according to the out-of-Africa theory—they spread across the globe. "This might sound funny coming from a scientist," says Berger, "but I think the emotive impact of these footprints is the most powerful message. It's incredibly exciting to put your foot into that print. This is from the time period from which every living human inherited his genetic potential. This is in fact one of us."

THE NEW YORK TIMES

Tuesday, October 29, 1996

Playing of Flute May Have Graced Neanderthal Fire

By JOHN NOBLE WILFORD

In the evening by firelight in their caves and rock shelters, the Neanderthals sometimes relaxed to the sound of music after a hard day at the hunt. They took material at hand, a cave bear's thigh bone, and created a flute. With such a simple instrument, these stocky, heavy-browed Neanderthals, extinct close relatives of humans, may have given expression to the fears, longings and joys of their prehistoric lives.

The image of Neanderthals as flautists, as having any ability for musical expression, was once beyond imagining. But a discovery in a cave in Slovenia, announced yesterday, evokes such a possible image, much to the surprise of archeologists and paleoanthropologists.

And if Neanderthals indeed made music of any kind, could this be indirect evidence that they also possessed some talent for language and articulate speech? It has been assumed that a lack of advanced communication skills was a critical disadvantage in their competition with modern *Homo sapiens*, who seem to have driven Neanderthals to extinction in Europe by 30,000 years ago.

Digging in the cave sediments last year, Dr. Ivan Turk, a paleontologist at the Slovenian Academy of Sciences in Ljubljana, found among the buried stone tools a small piece of a juvenile bear femur. It was perforated with four round holes. Two of the holes were intact; the other two, at either end of the bone, were incomplete. Presumably the ends had been chewed by animals or eroded over time.

The straight alignment of the holes, all on one side, suggests they were made not by gnawing animals but by the Neanderthals, probably using an animal-tooth punch. Neanderthals apparently occupied the cave, Divje Babe I, near Idrija in northwestern Slovenia, as a hunting camp.

Since the object resembled bone flutes found at other European and Asian sites of modern humans, usually dated from 22,000 to 35,000 years ago, Dr. Turk concluded that this could also be a flute, which would mean it was the first musical instrument ever to be associated with Neanderthals.

A team of Canadian and American researchers, including a high school student from Queens, has now established that the artifact is at least 43,000 years old, perhaps as much as 82,000 years old. If so, the researchers said, the bone flute is the oldest known musical instrument.

The findings were reported in Denver by Dr. Bonnie Blackwell of Queens College of the City University of New York. Other members of the team of geologists were Dr. Turk; Dr. Joel I. Blickstein of Queens College; Dr. Henry P. Schwarcz of McMaster University in Hamilton, Ontario; and Beverly Lau, who was a student at Robert F. Kennedy High School in Flushing, Queens, at the time.

Dr. Blackwell said the dates were determined by analyzing enamel from five cave bear teeth found in the same sedimentary layer with the putative flute. Objects of such antiquity cannot be dated by the usual radiocarbon techniques. Instead, the teeth were tested using a dating technology, electron spin resonance, that measures the small amounts of radiation absorbed by objects since their burial in the ground.

Miss Lau, now a freshman at the State University of New York at Binghamton, prepared the specimens for dating by separating the enamel from the dentine in each tooth. Her work was done under Dr. Blackwell's supervision, and the analysis was conducted in a nuclear reactor at McMaster University. A more detailed description of the research is to be published later in the journal *Geoarchaeology*.

The wide divergence in the estimated ages for the teeth, Dr. Blackwell said, reflected the researchers' uncertainty about how much moisture the cave floor has been exposed to. If the teeth had been subjected to excessive amounts of water, they would have absorbed less radiation; this could result in a too-low age estimate. Other evidence in the cave suggested that it has seen alternating periods of very dry and very wet conditions over the past 100,000 years. Further tests on more teeth and using other techniques are planned to narrow the uncertainty about the age.

At first, the purpose of the research was simply to date the teeth of the cave bears, animals that became extinct about 35,000 years ago. Then, after more explorations, Dr. Turk found the femur with the four holes. Examining the well-cemented sediment overlying the femur, he felt sure that the bone could not have settled into the layer with Neanderthal tools from some higher level.

"All of a sudden," she recalled, "our work went from being important to being exceedingly important. We were dating a site with a musical instrument, the only one ever found in a Neanderthal context."

Few subjects in human evolution are more puzzling than those concerning the nature and fate of the Neanderthals. They were shorter and stockier than most modern *Homo sapiens*, but were otherwise similar in anatomy and had a braincase as large or larger. They seemed to show none of the aptitude for art displayed by the cave painters who were their contemporaries and successors. But Neanderthals occupied a wide swath of the earth's surface, from the Atlantic coast to the Middle East and Central Asia and from northern Germany to Gibraltar, during their heyday 70,000 to 30,000 years ago.

Modern humans are thought by most scientists to have originated in Africa 150,000 to 200,000 years ago; they migrated to Europe about 40,000 years ago. Then the Neanderthals lost out in the competition with modern humans and disappeared.

Dr. Erik Trinkaus, an anthropologist at the University of New Mexico in Albuquerque, who is an authority on Neanderthals, said the discovery could have important implications for understanding these mysterious human relatives.

The only other such artifact of a possibly comparable age, he said, is a piece of bone found at a cave on the coast of Libya. It could have been a simple flute or a whistle and was associated with an apparently non-Neanderthal archaic human species.

If the interpretation of the new discovery is correct, Dr. Trinkaus said, "it reinforces the basic humanness of Neanderthals, even though they were different from modern humans with a different life style."

The discovery might also settle the issue of whether Neanderthals were capable of some simple speech. "I can't imagine a group having conscious music without having language," he said.

Dr. Philip G. Chase, an archeologist at the University of Pennsylvania Museum of Archeology and Anthropology, said the artifact record for early music was too sparse to allow for any definite connections yet between music and the evolution of intelligence, language and symbolic thinking.

"Music could be an esthetic early people developed, and only later it became fused with symbolism," Dr. Chase said. "But this flute, if that's what it is, certainly is intriguing. Music today is associated with symbolism. Whether that was the case at this earlier time is open to question."

DISCOVER

April 1998

New Women of the Ice Age

BY HEATHER PRINGLE

Forget about hapless mates being dragged around by macho mammoth killers. The women of Ice Age Europe, it appears, were not mere cavewives but priestly leaders, clever inventors, and mighty hunters.

The Black Venus of Dolni Vestonice, a small, splintered figurine sensuously fashioned from clay, is an envoy from a forgotten world. It is all soft curves, with breasts like giant pillows beneath a masked face. At nearly 26,000 years old, it ranks among the oldest known portrayals of women, and to generations of researchers, it has served as a powerful—if enigmatic—clue to the sexual politics of the Ice Age.

Excavators unearthed the Black Venus near the Czech village of Dolní Vestonice in 1924, on a hillside among charred, fractured mammoth bones and stone tools.... Since the mid-nineteenth century, researchers had discovered more than a dozen similar statuettes in caves and open-air sites from France to Russia. All were cradled in layers of earth littered with stone and bone weaponry, ivory jewelry, and the remains of extinct Ice Age animals. All were depicted naked or nearly so. Collectively, they came to be known as Venus figurines, after another ancient bare-breasted statue, the Venus de Milo. Guided at least in part by prevailing sexual stereotypes, experts interpreted the meaning of the figurines freely. The Ice Age camps that spawned this art, they concluded, were once the domain of hardworking male hunters and secluded, pampered women who spent their days in idleness like the harem slaves so popular in nineteenth-century art.

... By the 1990s ... [archeologists] had shaded and refined their portrait of Ice Age life. Between 29,000 and 25,000 years ago, they concluded, wandering bands had passed the cold months of the year repeatedly at Dolní Vestonice. Armed with short-range spears, the men appeared to have been specialists in hunting tusk-wielding mammoths and other big game, hauling home great mountains of meat to feed their dependent mates and children....

... [However, recently] a small team of American archeologists has raised some serious doubts [about this scenario]. Amassing critical and previously overlooked evidence from Dolní Vestonice and the neighboring site of Pavlov, Olga Soffer, James Adovasio, and David Hyland now propose that human survival there had little to do with manly men hurling spears at big-game animals. Instead, observes Soffer, one of the world's leading authorities on Ice Age hunters and gatherers and an archeologist at the University of Illinois in Champaign–Urbana, it depended largely on women, plants, and a technique of hunting previously invisible in the archeological evidence— net hunting. "This is not the image we've always had of Upper Paleolithic macho guys out killing animals up close and personal," Soffer explains. "Net hunting is communal, and it involves the labor of children and women. And this has lots of implications."

...

Recent anthropological research ... [supports Soffer's contention]. By observing women in the few remaining hunter-gatherer societies and by combing historical accounts of tribal groups more thoroughly, anthropologists have come to realize how critical the female half of the population has always been to survival. Women and children have set snares, laid spring traps, sighted game and participated in animal drives and surrounds—forms of hunting that endangered neither young mothers nor their offspring. They dug starchy roots and collected other plant carbohydrates essential to survival. They even hunted, on occasion, with the projectile points traditionally deemed men's weapons....

... [T]he results [of those studies] are gradually reshaping our understanding of Ice Age society. The famous Venus figurines, say archeologists of the new school, were never intended as male pornography: Instead they may have played a key part in Upper Paleolithic rituals that centered on women. And such findings, pointing toward a more important role for Paleolithic women than had previously been assumed, are giving many researchers pause.

Like many of her colleagues, Soffer clearly relishes the emerging picture of Upper Paleolithic life. "I think life back then was a hell of a lot more egalitarian than it was with your later peasant societies," she says. "Of course the Paleolithic women were pulling their own weight."... "Very few archeologists are hunters," she notes, so it never occurred to most of them to look into the mechanics of hunting dangerous tusked animals. They just accepted the ideas they'd inherited from past work.

... Soffer began studying Upper Paleolithic sites on the Russian and Eastern European plains. To her surprise, the famous mammoth bone beds were strewn with cumbersome body parts, such as 220-pound skulls, that sensible hunters would generally abandon. Moreover, the bones exhibited widely differing degrees of weathering, as if they had sat on the ground for varying lengths of time. To Soffer, it looked suspiciously as if Upper Paleolithic hunters had simply camped next to places where the pachyderms had perished naturally—such as water holes or salt licks—and mined the bones for raw materials.

... ... There the men spent more time scavenging bones and ivory from mammoth carcasses than they did risking life and limb by attacking 6,600-pound pachyderms with short-range spears. "If one of these Upper Paleolithic guys killed a mammoth, and occasionally they did," concedes Soffer dryly, "they probably didn't stop talking about it for ten years."

But if Upper Paleolithic families weren't often tucking into mammoth steaks, what were they hunting and how? Soffer found the first unlikely clue in 1991, while sifting through hundreds of tiny clay fragments recovered from the Upper Paleolithic site of Pavlov, which lies just a short walk from Dolní Vestonice. Under a magnifying lens, Soffer noticed something strange on a few of the fragments: a series of parallel lines impressed on their surfaces. What could have left such a regular pattern? Puzzled, Soffer photographed the pieces, all of which had been unearthed from a zone sprinkled with wood charcoal that was radiocarbon-dated at between 27,000 and 25,000 years ago.

... Soffer's [colleague Jim] Adovasio, an archeologist at Mercyhurst College in Pennsylvania and an expert on ancient fiber technology, immediately recognized the impressions of plant fibers. On a few, he could actually discern a pattern of interlacing fibers—weaving.

Without a doubt, he said, he and Soffer were gazing at textiles or basketry. They were the oldest—by nearly 7,000 years—ever found....

... [After collecting additional samples] he and his Mercyhurst colleague David Hyland peered at the casts under a zoom stereomicroscope, measuring warps and wefts. Forty-three revealed impressions of basketry and textiles. Some of the latter were as finely woven as a modern linen tablecloth. But as Hyland stared at four of the samples, he noted something potentially more fascinating: impressions of cordage bearing weaver's knots, a technique that joins two lengths of cord and that is commonly used for making nets of secure mesh. It looked like a tiny shred of a net bag, or perhaps a hunting net.... Last fall, Adovasio spied the telltale impressions of Ice Age mesh on one of the new casts.

The mesh, measuring two inches across, is far too delicate for hunting deer or other large prey. But hunters at Dolní Vestonice could have set nets of this size to capture hefty Ice Age hares, each carrying some six pounds of meat, and other furbearers such as arctic fox and red fox. As it turns out, the bones of hares and foxes litter camp floors at Dolní Vestonice and Pavlov. Indeed, this small game accounts for 46 percent of the individual animals recovered at Pavlov....

In many historical societies, [Soffer] observes, women played a key part in net hunting since the technique did not call for brute strength nor did it place young mothers in physical peril. Among Australian aborigines, for example, women as well as men knotted the mesh, laboring for as much as two or three years on a fine net. Among native North American groups, they helped lay out their handiwork on poles across a valley floor. Then the entire camp joined forces as beaters. Fanning out across the valley, men, women, and children alike shouted and screamed, flushing out game and driving it in the direction of the net. "Everybody and their mother could participate, says Soffer. "Some people were beating, others were screaming or holding the net. And once you got the net on these animals, they were immobilized. You didn't need brute force. You could club them, hit them any old way."

People seldom returned home empty-handed....

... Such findings, agree Soffer and Adovasio, reveal just how shaky the most widely accepted reconstructions of Upper Paleolithic life are. "These terribly stilted interpretations," says Adovasio, "with men hunting big animals all the time and the poor females waiting at home for these guys to bring home the bacon—what crap."

In her home outside Munich, Linda Owen finds other faults with this traditional image. Owen, an American born and raised, specializes in the microscopic analysis of stone tools. In her years of work, she often noticed that many of the tools made by hunters who roamed Europe near the end of the Upper Paleolithic era, some 18,000 to 12,000 years ago, resembled pounding stones and other gear for harvesting and processing plants....

...

Were Upper Paleolithic women gathering plants? The archeological literature was mostly silent on the subject. Few archeobotanists, Owen found, had ever looked for plant seeds and shreds in Upper Paleolithic camps. Most were convinced such efforts would be futile in sites so ancient. At University College London, however, Owen reached a determined young archeobotanist, Sarah Mason, who had analyzed a small sample of charcoal-like remains from a 26,390-year-old hearth at Dolní Vestonice.

The sample held more than charcoal. Examining it with a scanning electron microscope, Mason and her colleagues found fragments of fleshy plant taproots with distinctive secretory cavities—trademarks of the daisy and aster family, which boasts several species with edible roots. In all likelihood, women at Dolní Vestonice had dug the roots and cooked them into starchy meals. And they had very likely simmered other plant foods too. Mason and her colleagues detected a strange pulverized substance in the charred sample. It looked as if the women had either ground plants into flour and then boiled the results to make gruel or pounded vegetable material into a mush for their babies. Either way, says Soffer, the results are telling. "They're stuffing carbohydrates."

Owen is pursuing the research further. "If you do look," she says, "you can find things." At her urging, colleagues at the University of Tübingen are now analyzing Paleolithic hearths for botanical remains as they unearth them. Already they have turned up more plants, including berries, all clearly preserved after thousands of years. In light of these findings, Owen suggests that it was women, not men, who brought home most of the calories to Upper Paleolithic families. Indeed, she estimates that if Ice Age females collected plants, bird eggs, shellfish, and edible insects, and if they hunted or trapped small game and participated in the hunting of large game—as northern women did in historical times—they most likely contributed 70 percent of the consumed calories.

Moreover, some women may have enjoyed even greater power, judging from the most contentious relics of Ice Age life: the famous Venus figurines. Excavators have recovered more than 100 of the small statuettes, which were crafted between 29,000 and 23,000 years ago from such enduring materials as bone, stone, ander, ivory, and fired clay. The figurines share a strange blend of abstraction and realism. They bare prominent breasts, for example, but lack nipples. Their bodies are often minutely detailed down to the swaying lines of their backbones and the tiny rolls of flesh—fat folds— beneath their shoulder blades, but they often lack eyes, mouths, and any facial expression. For years researchers viewed them as a male art form. Early anthropologists, after all, had observed only male hunters carving stone, ivory, and other hard materials. Females were thought to lack the necessary strength. Moreover, reasoned experts, only men would take such loving interest in a woman's body. Struck by the voluptuousness of the small stone, ivory, and clay bodies, some researchers suggested they were Ice Age erotica, intended to be touched and fondled by their male makers. The idea still lingers. In the 1980s for example, the well-known American paleontologist Dale Guthrie wrote a scholarly article comparing the postures of the figurines with the provocative poses of *Playboy* centerfolds.

But most experts now dismiss such contentions. Owen's careful scouring of ethnographic sources, for example, revealed that women in arctic and subarctic societies did indeed work stone and ivory on occasion. And there is little reason to suggest the figurines figured as male erotica. The Black Venus, for example, seems to have belonged to a secret world of ceremony and ritual far removed from everyday sexual life.

The evidence, says Soffer, lies in the raw material from which the Black Venus is made. Clay objects sometimes break or explode when fired, a process called thermal-shock fracturing. Studies conducted by Pamela Vandiver of the Smithsonian Institution have demonstrated that the Black Venus and other human and animal figurines recovered from Dolní Vestonice—as well as nearly 2,000 fired ceramic pellets that litter the site—were made from a local clay that is resistant to thermal-shock fracturing. But many of the figurines, including the celebrated Black Venus, bear the distinctive jagged branching splinters created by thermal shock. Intriguingly, the fired clay pellets do not.

Curious, Vandiver decided to replicate the ancient firing process. Her analysis of the small Dolní Vestonice kilns revealed that they had been fired to temperatures around 1450 degrees Fahrenheit—similar to those of an ordinary hearth. So Vandiver set about making figurines of local soil and firing them in a similar earthen kiln, which a local archeological crew had built nearby. To produce thermal shock, she had to place objects larger than half an inch on the hottest part of the fire; moreover, the pieces had to be so wet they barely held their shape.

To Vandiver and Soffer, the experiment—which was repeated several times back at the Smithsonian Institution—suggests that thermal shock was no accident. "Stuff can explode naturally in the kiln," says Soffer, "or you can make it explode. Which was going on at Dolní Vestonice? We toyed with both ideas. Either we're dealing with the most inept potters, people with two left hands, or they are doing it on purpose. And we reject the idea that they were totally inept, because other materials didn't explode. So what are the odds that this would happen only with a very particular category of objects?"

These exploding figurines could well have played a role in rituals, an idea supported by the location of the kilns. They are situated far away from the dwellings, as ritual buildings often are. Although the nature of the ceremonies is not clear, Soffer speculates that they might have served as divination rites for discerning what the future held. "Some stuff is going to explode. Some stuff is not going to explode. It's evocative, like picking petals off a daisy. She loves me, she loves me not."

Moreover, ritualists at Dolní Vestonice could have read significance into the fracturing patterns of the figurines. Many historical cultures, for example, attempted to read the future by a related method called scapulimancy. In North America, Cree ceremonialists often placed the shoulder blade, or scapula, of a desired animal in the center of a lodge. During the ceremonies, cracks began splintering the bone: A few of these fractures leaked droplets of fat. To Cree hunters, this was a sign that they would find game if they journeyed in the directions indicated by the cracks.

Venus figurines from other sites also seem to have been cloaked in ceremony. "They were not just something made to look pretty," says Margherita Mussi, an archeologist at the University of Rome–La Sapienza who studies Upper Paleolithic figurines. Mussi notes that several small statuettes from the Grimaldi Cave carvings of southern Italy, one of the largest troves of Ice Age figurines ever found in Western Europe, were carved from rare materials, which the artists obtained with great difficulty, sometimes through trade or distant travel. The statuettes were laboriously whittled and polished, then rubbed with ocher, a pigment that appears to have had ceremonial significance, suggesting that they could have been reserved for special events like rituals.

The nature of these rites is still unclear. But Mussi is convinced that women took part, and some archeologists believe they stood at the center. One of the clearest clues, says Mussi, lies in a recently rediscovered Grimaldi figurine known as Beauty and the Beast. This greenish yellow serpentine sculpture portrays two arched bodies facing away from each other and joined at the head, shoulders, and lower extremities. One body is that of a Venus figurine. The other is a strange creature that combines the triangular head of a reptile, the pinched waist of a wasp, tiny arms, and horns. "It is clearly not a creature of this world," says Mussi.

The pairing of woman and supernatural beast, adds Mussi, is highly significant. "I believe that these women were related to the capacity of communicating with a different world," she says. "I think they were believed to be the gateway to a different dimension." Possessing powers that far surpassed others in their communities, such women may have formed part of a spiritual elite, rather like the shamans of ancient Siberia. As intermediaries between the real and spirit worlds, Siberian shamans were said to be able to cure illnesses and intercede on behalf of others for hunting success. It is possible that Upper Paleolithic women performed similar services for their followers.

Although the full range of their activities is unlikely ever to be known for certain, there is good reason to believe that Ice Age women played a host of powerful roles—from plant collectors and weavers to hunters and spiritual leaders. And the research that suggests those roles is rapidly changing our mental images of the past. For Soffer and others, these are exciting times. "The data do speak for themselves," she says finally. "They answer the questions we have. But if we don't envision the questions, we're not going to see the data."

DISCOVER

January 1997

Art in Australia, 60,000 Years Ago

BY SHANTI MENON

In Aboriginal lore, some sandstone outcroppings in northwest Australia mark the spot where a spirit called Jinmium, attempting to flee her pursuer, turned herself into stone. Jinmium is also the site, archeologists reported last year, of the world's earliest known art. Carved into the face of a 13-foot-tall sandstone monolith, and into many surrounding boulders, are thousands of shallow circular depressions, typically an inch across and half as deep. The marks were made at least 60,000 years ago—that's twice as old as any European cave painting.

Richard Fullagar, an archeologist at the Australian Museum in Sydney, first came upon the site in 1992, while surveying the area with his wife, geologist Leslie Head, but at that time he didn't know how old it was. "I was stunned by the density of these things," he says. "There are rocks the size of a Volkswagen that are totally pecked with these markings." The marks were apparently made with pieces of quartz about the size of a tennis ball, which Fullagar has also found at the site. He estimates that each mark took a half hour to an hour to make. That means many thousands of *Homo*-hours went into creating the oeuvre at Jinmium.

The site's significance remains mysterious. Though simple in form, the marks seem to be part of some larger, more complex system that extends over about 62 acres. Boulders covered with the gouges form parallel lines or arcs stretching hundreds of yards, connecting different rock shelters, or converging on a rock tunnel just big enough for a person to squeeze through.

Fullagar has also found a similar site some 20 miles north, called Granyilpi. Curiously, says Fullagar, in aboriginal mythology the spirit Jinmium began her journey at Granyilpi and ended it at Jinmium. There is nothing in aboriginal lore, though, about the origin or significance of the marks.

When Fullagar began excavating around the base of the tall sandstone monolith, he found that the marks on its surface continued down about three feet underground. He also found stone tools, apparently older than the markings, in deeper sediment layers around the monolith. Fullagar had some of the sediments dated through thermoluminescence, a technique for determining how long ago quartz grains were buried and began accumulating energy released by radioactive elements. The lowest—and presumably oldest—marks on the monolith appear to be about 60,000 years old, judging from the age of the sediments that buried them. The stone tools don't have an exact date, but were found below sediments that are 116,000 years old.

Fullagar's discovery pushes back the date of colonization of Australia—traditionally placed at 60,000 years ago—to perhaps more than 116,000 years ago. That was just about when modern humans supposedly emerged from Africa, according to the latest genetic evidence. If Fullagar's dates are right, the Africans must have crossed Asia and reached Australia very quickly indeed. Or else molecular biologists don't have the departure date right.

6

THE FUTURE:
PROGNOSTICATIONS AND PREDICAMENTS

We humans have been very successful as a species if population numbers and geographic spread are any indicators of success. We have outstripped our closest ape cousins in fertility; they barely hang on in small patches of forest in Africa and Southeast Asia. The facts in this case are these: From studies of total fertility rate (TFR) over time, to arrive at the number of humans the planet holds today (over 6 billion people) we had to have bred with an average TFR of 6 children per woman. However, populations living in urban environments by 1998 have reduced their TFR to about 3.3 and this number is falling. What does this situation mean to the future of our species? Today every ten seconds the world's population increases by 27 people. If an even lower TFR of only 2.6 children is achieved by 2150 the world population size could still be as much as 27 billion people. By further reducing the TFR by only one child per woman to 1.6 children, world population size would be reduced to only 3.6 billion. What are the potential consequences of such growth or, for that matter, if the TFR falls to 1.6, the loss of numbers of people? As world economies depend upon steady growth, would we face disasters at either end of this range of possibilities?

The pollution of land, water, and air and the destruction of many things that use earth's environments are significant problems. Old Malthusian projections reappear: too many people, too few resources to maintain them adequately. But what is adequate anyway? Is our over-consuming of nonrenewable resources way of life doomed under any circumstance, or can our technology pull us out of the mess we have created? Based on what we know of our past, can we make any reasonable projections for our future? This last chapter explores a few of the situations of the modern human condition and some of the ideas we have about where we go from here.

Coming up with new ideas quickly is a unique human feature. True, the apes and even some of the monkeys have shown us how innovative they can be, but for a new idea to spread among them takes great concentration. While we may think fast, it is also a sobering thought to realize from past history that much of what the human brain has concocted has been nonsense. The flat earth and the rejection of gravity are only two examples of a thinking process gone awry. Even today, at times, we think too fast and jump on popular bandwagons too eagerly without giving real thought to the consequences. If we are to make real progress toward the solution of our many problems, maybe an ape-paced thought process is preferable. In "Think Tank: Lofty Ideas That May Be Losing Altitude," Janny Scott of the *New York Times* looks at some of our more recent ideas and finds that in many cases we are still making the same mistakes.

Ecological issues that face us today are constantly in the news. Global warming, ozone depletion, El Nino, and La Nina are conditions that may be caused by but certainly affect the ever burgeoning human population. In "You Can't Beat Mother Nature," author Dorian Sagan reviews two recent books for the *New York Times* that address these and other problems, and concludes that, perhaps, the most important knowledge the current exploitive human can gain from all this is the recognition of his own stupidity.

Just how much of our behavior is actually controlled by our genes? Sociobiologists claim that genes influence everything we do and that behavior along with anatomical structure should be viewed as an adaptation. Arthur Jensen, an educational psychologist at the University of California, Berkeley, was not the first person to link IQ scores to specific groups of people, but in the 1960s he certainly made an impact with his published findings, which caused many to brand him as a racist. Most recently, authors Richard Herrnstein and Charles Murray, in their book *The Bell Curve*, have resurrected some of Jensen's arguments by opting strongly for genes rather than environment as the primary determinant for a person's success or failure to achieve. In "The Bell Curve, Revisited by Scholars," Michael M. Weinstein of the *New York Times* reports on criticisms of the Bell Curve hypothesis.

The Human Genome Project promises to unfold many answers about the relationship of genetics to the human condition, ranging from individual susceptibility to various diseases to those driving forces behind our behavior and mentality. The first stage of this new genetic technology is to discover the genetic links by unraveling the DNA code. This scientists are doing at incredible speed. The authors of *The Bell Curve* may have missed the mark in proving their case, but genes may still lurk undetected that could revive the issue at a more sophisticated level. In "First Gene to Be Linked with High Intelligence Is Reported Found," Nicholas Wade of the *New York Times* reports on a recent discovery of a gene that purports to do just that.

Understanding what genes do will unquestionably have great impact on our future. Hardly anyone will argue that the discovery of human genes that contribute to disease is bad. As one consequence of this research a new era of preventive medicine promises more effective drug therapies for suffering individuals. Other offshoots of genetic research, however, are more controversial. *New York Times* columnist Nicholas Wade, in his article "In the Hunt for Useful Genes, a Lot Depends on 'Snips,'" describes the Human Genome Project, the search for variations in the DNA code (SNPs) and some of the social concerns this growing body of information raises.

Part of the new research on the human genome shows promise in elucidating past human events. SNPs, as reported in Nicholas Wade's article, can tell us something about the timing and patterning of human migrations. But what if finding this information makes our lives more difficult? What if it conflicts with long-held beliefs about our origins and our place in the cosmos? In "Science and the Native American Cosmos," Native American scholar Jace Weaver, a lawyer and a visiting lecturer in Native American studies at Yale University, writes to the *New York Times* with some of these concerns in mind.

Yet another controversial outcome of genetic research is the potential to change what we have inherited. The new reproductive biology that takes sex out of the bedroom and into the laboratory has a chilling effect on many people. The possibility that parents one day can design their children's genes to suit themselves has moral and ethical considerations that humans have never before had to face. In "Scientists Brace for Changes in Path of Human Evolution," Gina Kolata describes this new research and the potential it has for changing the path of human evolution.

As a species we are a product of evolution. Along the evolutionary pathway selection has favored individuals who possessed higher levels of technological skills and abilities. Advances in technology have, in turn, altered the path of evolution in favor of individuals who could use this technology to their best advantage: Brute strength was out, brain power was in. Concluding this chapter, Karen Wright of *Discover* magazine, in her article "Human in the Age of Mechanical Reproduction," shows us that we are approaching a technological milestone that has the potential to alter the notion of Darwinian fitness. The new reproductive biology promises designer children for all, fertile or not, without the bother of sex or the trouble of a nine-month pregnancy.

Saturday, November 1, 1997

Think Tank: Lofty Ideas
That May Be Losing Altitude

BY JANNY SCOTT

The *New York Times* asked six scholars what they thought was the Most Overrated Idea. Here are their responses, compiled by Janny Scott.

Intelligence Testing

*Howard Gardner, Professor, Harvard Graduate School of Education,
and pioneer of the theory of multiple intelligences*

The most overrated idea is that our intelligence is an entity we can measure by sticking a mental dipstick into our mind/brain. We pull it out and we read 80 or 100 or whatever. Psychologists can tell us how smart we are, or maybe now geneticists. Then there's a "Bell Curve" twist that says society's problems are due to the dummies.

The biological, psychological and anthropological evidence is strongly against this unitary notion of intelligence. There are many human intelligences, nobody is equally good at all, and cultural opportunities determine which are developed and to what extent.

But there has been a conspiracy between the industry of psychometrics and the seductiveness of a familiar word. And that conspiracy yields this ubiquitous conviction that there's a single thing called smartness.

Repression

Frederick Crews, Professor emeritus of English,
University of California, Berkeley.

According to this notion, one represses a memory because it is profoundly traumatic and unacceptable to the conscious mind and this causes continuing psychological damage. Thus, if we want to make people whole again, we need to get at the early experiences that they have not been able either to remember or to forget. And so we get psychoanalytic therapy.

This kind of therapy is going to be more prolonged and more expensive than any other kind. But there is no evidence whatsoever that the pursuit of repressed memories is any more therapeutic than placebo treatments.

Over the past dozen years, we've had a much stronger concept of repression, one that even Freud would have hesitated to endorse. We now have innumerable cases of adults who, until they entered psychotherapy, had the impression that they had been raised in loving families and had been treated in normal ways. But thanks to the ministrations of therapists who believe that a whole range of adult symptoms can probably be best explained by the repression of childhood sexual abuse, these people emerge from therapy drastically alienated not only from their families but also from their own selves. In all but the tiniest minority of cases, these accusations are false.

Modernism

Witold Rybczynski, Professor of urbanism, University of Pennsylvania

There was the idea, in the beginning of the 20th century, that we lived in a different sort of time, loosely called the modern period. In architecture, painting, literature, music, there was a feeling that the modern period was so different that we really needed to rethink all these fields. At the end of the century, we're sort of going back and saying maybe we should be picking up the pieces.

There was this whole flurry of experimental writing, which seems to have gotten us nowhere, so we're going back to narrative in writing, just as we're going back to ornament and symbolism in architecture. Even in town planning, there is this idea that we should revisit some of the traditional ideas of towns.

Post-Modernism

Richard Rorty, Philosopher, University of Virginia

The first thing that comes to mind is post-modernism. It's one of these terms that has been used so much that nobody has the foggiest idea what it means. It means one thing in philosophy, another thing in architecture and nothing in literature. It would be nice to get rid of it. It isn't exactly an idea; it's a word that pretends to stand for an idea. Or maybe the idea that one ought to get rid of is that there is any need to get beyond modernity.

Eternal Life

*Alexander Nehamas, Professor in the humanities
and philosophy, Princeton University*

The idea that there is such a thing as an eternal life and that it is in most ways more important than this life—though it has produced a number of great goods—I think has generally caused immensely greater misery than it has helped the world.

First of all, it has completely devalued, for many of those who believe in it, their present life. Second, it has made many of those people who believe in it live in constant fear and guilt for what's going to happen to them afterward. And it has prevented them from doing anything to get rid of that fear and guilt by acting right because, if anything, they will get their just deserts later on.

Faith in the eternal life, which means faith in an absolute justification if you are on the right side, has caused some of the worst treatment of human beings by other human beings.

THE NEW YORK TIMES

Sunday, August 31, 1997

You Can't Beat Mother Nature

By Dorion Sagan

We cannot help being interested in the ecological effects of the rampant increase in human beings. The moral status of this growth is paradoxical. Our plundering of energy-rich fossils laid down by previous life-forms made possible the technological innovations of the Industrial Revolution. Whatever aspersions one may cast on the "naturalness" of such plundering, it has become a lifeline, continuing to fuel the agricultural-industrial complex that supports most of this planet's increasingly urban population. Governments desire growth—slow growth—as a provider of jobs, a way to stoke the global economy. People concerned with global ecology, however, deride the ideology of growth and point to the trail of natural destruction it has caused. Health and happiness, they insist, can be had only by going back to nature, studying it for the secrets of a sustainable technology and living within a more-than-human richness that was the norm until nature became afflicted by the cancer of humanity. Unfortunately, like many middle-class intellectual polarizations, the debate between ecological conservatives and economic liberals is too much about taking sides and preaching to the converted and too little about listening to other views.

Two recent books, *Kinship to Mastery: Biophilia in Human Evolution and Development*, by Stephen R. Kellert, and *Biomimicry: Innovation Inspired by Nature*, by Janine M. Benyus, add to the debate. The sophisticated, almost pro-growth angle of Benyus shows the great potential profitability of copying some of nature's time-tested, nonpolluting, room-temperature manufacturing and computing technologies. The colors of Benyus, a splendid Stevensville, Mont., science writer with a grasp of several sciences, contain far more shades of green than of chrome. Rhetorically at least, the ultimate attraction of technologies like the 3-billion-year-old photosynthesis that scientists are now trying to "biomimic" is that the techniques nature has evolved are more sophisticated and efficient, less disruptive and destructive than the Promethean pyrotechnics that have made humanity the new kid on the evolutionary block. Like someone who has made a fortune trading fast-growing speculative stocks but must now provide for her retirement by switching to safer, lower-yielding bonds, if we don't switch to safer modes of sustenance we will take a major hit, perhaps even extinction, because the logic of ecology suggests that the fossil-fuel economies that have got us this far will soon be bankrupt.

That may be correct. The artful science of living nature makes the old physics of regular celestial motions, once believed to be perfect and divine, look robotically stupid in comparison. Science, whose great early advances came in uncovering the relatively predictable activities of inanimate objects, has lately found success in examining more complex and chaotic structures, the shiniest example of which, of course, is life. The social critic Walter Benjamin pointed out that sometimes the extreme case, not the average, is exemplary. And the theoretical biologist Robert Rosen suggests that biology may be the more generally instructive science, and physics a local application of it.

Modern science, like law, requires a preponderance of evidence to convince us. In *Kinship to Mastery*, Kellert, who teaches environmental studies at Yale, uses a method that is the antithesis of that—he tells anecdotes: a boy brought back from despair at the death of his father by the gift of a dog from his sister; a parrot-toting prisoner who becomes an expert on psittacines; a yuppie couple whose marriage is saved by a trip to an island off Nova Scotia, and whose son grows up in a new New York that emerges "at the forefront of a new environmental covenant" and has, for example, a "biopark established along an abandoned industrial shoreline in the South Bronx" to excellent effect. Unlike the often seen, numbingly impersonal statistics on the biological decrepitude of our planet, these anecdotal fictions strike home personally. Kellert's vignettes wake us up to smell the flowers—the ones that are left.

Benyus shows once and for all the utter technological superiority of would-be "lower" life-forms: the underwater superglue made by mussels; a spider's dragline silk that, ounce for ounce, is five times as strong as steel and five times as impact-resistant as bulletproof Kevlar; and bears and chimpanzees that collect medicinal herbs. Imagine an undiscovered planet in our solar system consisting of intensely advanced life-forms that had perfected waste management, parallel shape-based molecular computing and the processing of nanotechnological materials billions of years ago. That planet is our own. Benyus has had the wit to recognize nature's own genius and make scientists' attempts to copy it the theme of a popular book.

Amusingly, however, when she talks about the "living, breathing examples of sustainability" held up by proponents of biomimicry as natural models that we humans should now emulate, she uses a technological metaphor: At this crucial juncture in our evolution as a species, natural technology is "lighting the runway home." This can be read as an unconscious nod to the petroleum-based colossus involved at many levels in the printing and distribution of books, and to the fact that any truly powerful program devised to subvert the present "unsustainable" ecological impact of humans is likely to employ the very technology (like petroleum-fed global transportation) it criticizes.

These two valuable and stimulating books bring us to a brutal question. How will we get back to nature? Benyus evokes a simple ecological "canon" she says can be used as a template for our technology. A natural system should run on sunlight. It should use only the energy it needs. It should fit form to function. It should recycle everything. It should bank on diversity (but after fire, nuclear explosion and other crises, certain organisms grow wildly, priming the area for followers). It should curb excess from within (all right, but excess creates the luxury that leads to innovation, and new problems). And it should be beautiful (why not?).

This is a noble list. What needs to be clarified, however, is the larger evolutionary perspective. The ecological "canon" of emulatable processes displayed by nature cannot be conflated with nature per se. We are about to embark on an often-traveled ecological adjustment made by many organisms that, finding a formerly unused resource, grow wildly and then are forced to deal with the spoils, in every sense, of their victory. The energy from the sun that runs through all life is a Pandoran excess that cannot be closed up and kept tidy. The global environment, like Rome in its senescence, will always be open to organisms evolving new ways to plunder it. Like other pioneer species, but on a larger, global scale, we must now temper our populousness and promote a greater biodiversity of which we are only a smaller part, not because of any intrinsic evil but because of the dangers, mostly to ourselves, caused by our own fabulously innovative growth.

Billions of years ago, when cyanobacteria tapped into water as a source of hydrogen, the free oxygen they produced as waste was no evolutionary breath of fresh air. Rather, the reactive gas burned the tissues of all organisms that had not evolved to tolerate or use it, especially the creators, who found themselves in the midst of the gas. Our puritanical environmentalism needs a Swift to kick it. Nietzsche, who disparaged the use of mechanical rather than natural metaphors, observed over a century ago that "power makes stupid." Our ability to tap into Earth's resources to power our own growth has brought us to something even more annoying than the brink of collapse of population or standards of living; it has brought us face to face with our own stupidity. Books like these are valuable reminders that in the long run moderation pays.

THE NEW YORK TIMES

Saturday, October 11, 1997

The Bell Curve, Revisited by Scholars

By Michael M. Weinstein

The Bell Curve inflamed readers when it was published three years ago by arguing that economic and social success in America had become largely a matter of genes, not education, environment or other factors over which society might exert control. The chilling genes-are-destiny thesis, laced with racial overtones, was greeted with furious criticism. But much of the initial criticism was ill informed and driven by ideology.

It could hardly have been otherwise. The book's authors, Richard Herrnstein and Charles Murray, did not release their statistical findings—the only important original contributions in the book—for formal review by scholars before publication. Their runaround obstructed response by other social scientists, who needed time to appraise hundreds of pages of statistical analysis. Now, three years later, scholars have caught up, shattering the book's core claims.

Messrs. Herrnstein and Murray use statistical tools to determine whether differences in intelligence or environment better explain, for example, which individuals commit crimes, drop out of high school or wind up poor. The authors find that, in their all-white sample, low intelligence leads to social pathology. High intelligence leads to success. Family background plays a secondary role. That suggests that compensatory education and training are almost certain to fail.

That core finding would be devastating if true. But other scholars have now decisively shown that the book's evidence is riddled with mistakes. Two stand out.

The first error flows from biased statistics. The book tries to determine whether I.Q. or family background is a better predictor of success. I.Q. is easily measured. But family background is not. The authors' simplistic index incorporates parental income, education and job prestige, but leaves out numerous components of a child's upbringing.

That creates a statistical mirage, or bias, because statistical tests inevitably underestimate the impact of factors that are hard to measure. Mistakes in measuring family background obliterate the ability of statisticians to detect its impact on future success. Thus, as James Heckman of the University of Chicago has convincingly argued, the book's finding that family background is a weak precursor of success reflects its biased methods rather than the workings of American society.

Also compelling is evidence about the second notable error—that the authors' measure of intelligence is by no means immutable, as their thesis requires. Prof. Derek Neal of the University of Chicago and Prof. William Johnson of the University of Virginia have shown that scores on the measurement used by Mr. Herrnstein and Mr. Murray, the Armed Forces Qualification Test, depend on how much schooling individuals have completed. Put simply, the more students study in school, the better they do on the test. So what the authors call immutable intelligence turns out to be what others call skills—indeed, teachable skills.

This mistake turns the message of the book on its head. Instead of its sighing surrender to supposed genetic destiny for poor children, there's a corrected message: Teach them.

THE NEW YORK TIMES

Thursday, May 14, 1998

First Gene to Be Linked
with High Intelligence Is Reported Found

BY NICHOLAS WADE

Psychologists using a new genetic technique have found a gene associated with high intelligence. The technique, they say, should help to identify several more of the many genes thought to affect human intelligence and personality. If the work is confirmed by other researchers, it would be the first time that a gene contributing to intelligence had been found.

The new finding is a tender green shoot arising from the ashes of a long-smoldering debate about whether intelligence is determined by people's genes or by the circumstances of their upbringing. Many psychologists now believe there is clear evidence that heredity is important but not all powerful, and that genes account for about 50 percent or more of the variance in I.Q., or intelligence quotient. Variance is a statistical measure of how widely a quality varies in a population.

The gene was pinpointed by studying about 50 students whose SAT scores were equivalent to an I.Q. score of 160 or higher, and by comparing their DNA with children of average I.Q.

The research, published in the current issue of the journal *Psychological Science*, was conducted by Dr. Robert Plomin, a leading American behavioral geneticist who works at the Institute of Psychiatry in London. His co-authors include Dr. David Lubinski and Dr. Camilla Benbow. Their talent search program, known as the Study of Mathematically Precocious Youth, supplied the test subjects.

Dr. Plomin has sought to move the debate forward by arguing that if genes for intelligence exist it should be possible to track some of them down through the powerful new genetic scanning techniques that have recently become available. Searching through a small part of the human genome, the long arm of chromosome 6, he found that a particular variant of a certain gene was twice as common in his sample of children with ultra-high I.Q.s than in those with average I.Q.s. The gene has a very small effect, accounting for about 2 percent of the variance, or 4 I.Q. points, Dr. Plomin said.

So slight an effect would be expected in a trait influenced by many genes. There might be 50 or more genes affecting intelligence, experts say, and a person with a high I.Q. would have the favorable versions of only some of these genes. Only half the children with high I.Q.s in Dr. Plomin's study had the intelligence-promoting form of the gene he detected.

Dr. Nathan Brody, a psychologist at Wesleyan University, said Dr. Plomin's finding was a small step in itself but of "enormous significance" if it proved to be the beginning of the detection of other genes that influence intelligence.

"I think his work is an important technical achievement," said Dr. John Kihlstrom, a psychologist at the University of California at Berkeley. "He has married the human genome technology with the study of behavioral genetics." Dr. Kihlstrom is the editor of the journal in which Dr. Plomin's study appeared. Dr. Kihlstrom said that Dr. Plomin is a leading figure in the field of behavior genetics and that the new report was "the first time that a gene has been associated with some specific aspect of cognition and behavior," with the exception of the gene governing the behavioral disorder known as Williams syndrome.

Another psychologist who studies the genetics of behavior, Dr. Thomas Bouchard of the University of Minnesota, said the new finding was "nice ordinary science without extravagant claims" but would require independent studies before being confirmed.

The genes Dr. Plomin has been seeking are those that affect intelligence in the broadest sense, known to psychologists as general cognitive ability. This is the quality that I.Q. tests seek to measure. Brain experts now believe that general cognitive ability is composed of many overlapping capabilities, like verbal and math skills.

The genetic variation Dr. Plomin found lies in an obscure but extremely powerful gene known as the I.G.F.2 receptor gene. The I.G.F.2, or insulin-like growth factor 2, is a multifaceted hormone about which little is known. Dr. Randy Jirtle, a molecular biologist at Duke University who studies the gene because of its involvement in cancer, said it might influence both the development and everyday metabolism of the brain, although neither role has been proved. At the least, Dr. Jirtle said, Dr. Plomin has hit on a "plausible candidate" for a gene that affects intelligence.

Dr. Mony De Leon, a neuroscientist at the New York University School of Medicine, said, "This is the first step of its kind, but a very small step, toward establishing what the inherited aspects of intelligence may be."

The variation found by Dr. Plomin and his team lies in a part of the gene's DNA that is trimmed away before the genetic message is translated into a working protein. Thus the variation probably cannot in itself affect intelligence but presumably lies next to some translated region that does.

The finding is a statistical association, not proof of causation, and requires several further steps to make the claim of an intelligence gene indisputable. Besides independent corroboration, biologists would wish to locate the translated part of the variant gene and understand how it affects intelligence.

Genetic variations like those Dr. Plomin is studying may be more common in some ethnic groups and less common in others. To prevent any ethnic effect from confounding the link between genes and intelligence, Dr. Plomin decided to confine his study to a single ethnic group, in this case white Americans.

The finding has no immediate practical importance, since the gene accounts for such a small percentage of intelligence. But Dr. Plomin says he expects to find many more such genes, including at least one on each of the 23 pairs of human chromosomes. Knowledge of these genes, and what they do, could in time help researchers understand the nature of intelligence, as well as learning disabilities and the intellectual decay that occurs in Alzheimer's disease.

But Dr. Kihlstrom said he feared a more immediate reaction. Despite the tiny effect of the gene, he said, "I confidently predict that within two months there will be genetic centers set up for profit to test parents for this gene." He said such centers would be a "crummy idea."

Dr. Plomin and his colleagues said they were well aware of the potentials for abuse of their finding, like discriminative genetic screening and assertions that genes determine everything. "Despite the new problems created by new findings," they wrote in their report, "it would be a mistake, and futile as well, to try to cut off the flow of knowledge and its benefits in order to avoid having to confront new problems."

THE NEW YORK TIMES

Tuesday, August 11, 1998

In the Hunt for Useful Genes, a Lot Depends on "Snips"

By Nicholas Wade

A new word is edging into the study of human genetics: the snip. Snips, variations in the DNA that make each individual unique, are the genetic determinants of health and disease. Because of machines that rapidly decode DNA, the chemical chain that embodies the genetic instructions, snips are at last becoming widely accessible.

Snips promise to yield two troves of information, one past and one present.

They will help population geneticists reconstruct the size and timing of the early human migrations that peopled the globe. And they should enable medical geneticists to trace elusive links between genes and disease, particularly the common diseases to which many genes contribute. With the use of snips, pharmaceutical companies hope to match drugs more precisely to an individual's unique genetic makeup.

The search for snips is an essential counterpart to the Human Genome Project, the attempt to decode or sequence all 3 billion letters of human DNA in the next 5 to 7 years. The human genome project largely ignores the variations in DNA that make each person unique. Based on analyzing the DNA of just a few individuals, it will provide a consensus sequence, meaning the DNA letter that is most commonly found at each of the 3 billion positions on the DNA chain.

Though the consensus sequence is of great interest to biologists trying to figure out the operation of the human genetic programming, medical geneticists are interested in the variations from the consensus because in them lies the answer as to why one person may succumb to a disease and another resist it.

The number of variations among 6 billion humans might seem impossibly large because in principle every letter in the genome can change, whether by chemical decay, a hit from stray radiation or a copying error. But in fact the variation is much more limited, with changes being commonly found only at particular sites in the DNA.

The reason is that by evolution's standards the human species is very young, a mere 100,000 years or so, and at about that time went through a population bottleneck of some 10,000 individuals.

"The blink of an eye since we left Africa hasn't been long enough to build up many common variations," said Dr. Eric S. Lander, a biologist at the Whitehead Institute in Boston and the principal proponent of a remarkable "snip chip" that could someday identify an individual's genetic variations.

"We have the level of variation expected from 10,000 people because we are just a little population that happened to grow big."

Most of the medically interesting variations in DNA are in the form of single changes to a nucleotide, the chemical units that make up the DNA chain. Changes that are commonly found, meaning in at least 1 percent of a population, are known as SNPs, or single nucleotide polymorphisms.

SNPs, pronounced snips, can exert dramatic effects. Sickle cell anemia is caused solely by the change of an A to a T (A, T, C and G are the symbols for the four chemical letters, or nucleotides, that make up the DNA alphabet) in one of the genes that specifies the hemoglobin protein of the red blood cells. Three variant spellings in the gene known as apolipoprotein E account for much of the risk for Alzheimer's disease.

SNPs occur in roughly one out of every 500 positions along the DNA chain. Because only 3 percent of the genome appears to be active in the body, the rest being generally of no known purpose, there are only some 200,000 snips in the genes that specify the working parts of the body's cells. The effective human genetic repertoire is apparently limited to combinations, very large though their number is, of this finite number of variations.

Biologists pursuing snips in parallel with the decoding of the human genome are headed in two main directions. One is the effort to measure how genetic variation is distributed around the globe, information that will help track prehistoric human migrations.

The Human Genome Diversity Project, headed by Luca Cavalli-Sforza of Stanford University, aims to collect DNA from at least 100 populations on each continent. But the project has been held up by objections that it would exploit the people who donated samples. In a recent review, a panel convened by the National Academy of Sciences endorsed the goals of the project but said more work should be done to address ethical concerns.

The other major use of snips is in tracing the genetic variations that contribute to health and disease. Diseases caused by defects in a single gene have been easy enough to trace because they are inherited in the simple patterns first described by Gregor Mendel, the founder of genetics, in the 19th century. But these Mendelian diseases tend to be quite rare. Most common maladies, like heart disease and schizophrenia, are thought to be caused by the defective versions of many genes acting in concert. Because each gene makes only a minor contribution to the disease, it is hard for geneticists to trace its effects even when they have large family pedigrees to work with.

The current method of mapping the human genome depends on the same kind of signpost or marker that is used in the forensic technique of DNA fingerprinting. But these markers, which consist of repetitive bits of DNA repeated a varying number of times in different individuals, are technically difficult to work with. So far, there has been very little success in digging out the genetic roots of multigene diseases.

Hence, considerable interest was aroused by a recent calculation that multigene diseases could be cracked through the snip approach. Its authors, Neil Risch of Stanford University and Kathleen Merikangas of Yale, said that a simple association study—comparing people with and without a given disease—would help pinpoint the contributory genes if enough snips could be identified along the DNA chain so that one would probably be in or near the causative genes.

Citing the Risch-Merikangas paper, Dr. Francis S. Collins, director of the human genome project at the National Institutes of Health, persuaded the directors of other N.I.H. divisions to join in financing a grand hunt for snips, based on the premise that genetic factors contribute to almost every human disease. The hunt began last January, at a cost of $10 million a year and with the goal of locating at least 100,000 snips spread out across the genome, which Dr. Collins calculates is the necessary number to tag most genes of possible interest.

Snips are also the basis of a fashionable new approach to drug design known as pharmacogenomics. The premise is that people respond differently to drugs based on their genetic makeup. With the use of snips, it should be possible to tailor drugs to patients, selecting the drug that works best for a person and excluding from drug trials the people likely to suffer side effects.

If the approach works, drug companies might end up selling fewer drugs, but could charge more for the tailored approach. Last year Abbott Laboratories made a $20 million deal with Genset, a Paris-based company, to discover 60,000 SNPs spread across the genome.

Once the snips are identified, they can be used for many purposes. A particularly striking application is that of the snip chip.

Made in a similar way to computer chips but incorporating DNA, the chip can be programmed to scan a DNA chain for specific sequences of letters. Chips are being developed by biologists at the Whitehead Institute and at Affymetrix in Santa Clara, Calif., with the ultimate purpose of scanning a person's whole DNA or genome for all medically significant snips.

Dr. Lander believes a single chip, or set of chips, could be programmed to sift the 6 million snips strung along the human genome to find the 200,000 snips occurring within the coding regions that actually affect the individual.

Such a chip could, in effect, sequence a person's genome in minutes by identifying all significant differences from the consensus sequence. It would also provide a kind of fate map, enabling a physician to assess the genetic strength of a person's constitution, the diseases to which they were vulnerable and perhaps their likely longevity.

At present, of course, the 200,000 coding snips are far from being identified, let alone understood in terms of their medical significance. Still, the snip chip is already under way. In May, Dr. Lander and his colleagues described a chip that can analyze 500 snips simultaneously with reasonable accuracy, and a 2,000-snip chip is also in development.

Dr. Lander views his concept of a whole genome chip as more a diagnostic than a predictive tool. People can already forecast their medical fate pretty accurately by noting their parents' ages and causes of death, he said.

The snip chip "is a way of teasing apart the causes of disease rather than predicting the future," Dr. Lander said. "For every spot on the chip, you need information and understanding, and that will take a long time."

As that understanding is acquired, however, the chips seem likely to intensify the existing problems of human genetics, such as how to counsel patients and how to insure that the information is not used to their detriment.

"This is a very major ethical issue, and ELSI has already decided to make this its highest priority," Dr. Collins said, referring to the branch of the human genome project that studies its ethical and legal consequences. "This ability to collect very large amounts of variation on individuals will be quickly upon us. It will empower people to take advantage of preventive strategies, but it could also be a nightmare of discriminatory information that could be used against people."

Of course, the links between snips and disease may prove more elusive than expected. A recent analysis of a gene that regulates fat metabolism and is thought to play a role in heart disease turned up an unexpectedly complex pattern of snips among the three populations surveyed. The pattern makes it less certain that association studies between snips and genes will pinpoint the genes involved in disease, said Dr. Andrew G. Clark of Pennsylvania State University, an author of the study.

In an article in the current issue of *Genome Research*, Dr. Kenneth M. Weiss, also of Penn State, warns of "unrealistic expectations of the questions that can be answered from genetic data."

Dr. Weiss notes that evolution acts on the phenotype, not the genotype, meaning on the organism that is produced from the genes, not the genes themselves. Although the genes carry a message as precise as the digital code of a computer program, the phenotype is tolerant of variation and survives with as wide a range of genetic instructions as possible.

Therefore, the link between genes and people may be somewhat fuzzier, Dr. Weiss suggests, than the crispness of a DNA sequence would suggest.

Science and the Native American Cosmos

By Jace Weaver

To the Editor:

Re "Indian Tribes' Creationists Thwart Archeologists" (front page, Oct. 22): The fear among most Native Americans about scientific testing of remains discovered by archeologists is not that it will disprove sacred accounts but that it will further desecrate the remains. DNA testing is opposed because it consumes the sample tested. If the real fear were that human origins in the Americas would prove to be the product of relatively recent migrations from Asia, why would tribes allow radiocarbon dating, which could lend credence to the same theory?

You say the Bering Strait theory, holding that America's native peoples came from Asia 10,000 or more years ago, is "embraced by virtually all archeologists." The so-called land bridge between Asia and North America is thought to have existed three times, beginning 70,000 years ago. It is a common joke in Indian country that the only physical evidence for a Bering Strait migration is a single fossil footprint, and that scientists cannot tell which direction it is heading.

The Bering Strait theory is simply that—a theory.

You say that "according to many Indian creation accounts, natives have always lived in the Americas after emerging onto the surface of the earth from a subterranean world of spirits." But Native tribes are possessed of a tremendous variety of cosmologies and religious traditions that often differ as much as Christianity differs from Hinduism. To homogenize them and juxtapose them with science is a disservice to all concerned.

Scientists Brace for Changes in Path of Human Evolution

BY GINA KOLATA

For years, molecular biologists and geneticists have trod gingerly around the most explosive topic of the new reproductive biology: purposely making genetic changes in people that would persist for generation after generation.

There were so many technological roadblocks to the process, called germline genetic engineering, that most scientists viewed it almost as science fiction. But now, as researchers rush past these roadblocks, a group of eminent molecular biologists and geneticists met here today on the leafy campus of the University of California at Los Angeles to confront the issue. Their goal was to discuss how, why and when germline engineering should proceed.

The scientists, leaders in the fields, were meeting on their own, with no government or other mandate to issue guidelines or regulations and, in fact, no wish to restrict their work. But they said it was time for science to confront its growing powers to shape human biology.

The public and even many scientists are unaware of how close science is to making germline engineering a reality, said Dr. Michael Rose, who studies the genetics of aging at the University of California at Irvine and was a speaker at the meeting.

He said the meeting would bring public attention to "one of the most important questions for the human species: the extent to which it will direct its own evolution."

It will, some day, be possible to give people genes to prevent them from developing certain diseases or to cure them of diseases that resist treatment, like cancer or AIDS. "I could imagine a child that never got a cold," said Dr.

John Campbell, a meeting organizer who is a theoretical evolutionary biologist and a professor of neurobiology at U.C.L.A. They could eventually add whole "cassettes" of genes that could confer enhanced intelligence or rid people of the plagues of aging, he said.

Unlike genetic therapies being experimented with today, in which scientists try to insert genes into specific body tissues, these genetic changes could become permanent, present in sperm and egg cells and passed from generation to generation.

Germline genetic engineering "really touches the essence of who we are, what it means to be human," said Dr. Gregory Stock, a conference organizer and director of the Science, Technology and Society program at U.C.L.A.'s Center for the Study of Evolution and the Origin of Life. "We are talking about intervening in the flow of genetic information from one generation to the next. We are talking about the relationship of human beings to their genetic heritage."

The speakers, drawn from the ranks of molecular biology and genetics, had the most august credentials: memberships in the National Academy of Science, a Nobel Prize, editorships of leading journals. Throughout the day, one after the other spoke about new possibilities and powerful new tools already under development to make human germline engineering happen.

No one could say with certainty when this new kind of genetic engineering could be put into practice. But they all agreed that seemingly insuperable technical barriers were falling year by year and many said they expected to see the techniques in use within 20 years.

As recently as 15 years ago, Dr. Campbell said, putting a cassette of genes together would have been a herculean task. Now, he added, it could be a project for graduate students.

Of course, once genetic germline engineering becomes technically feasible, researchers would want to conduct studies in animals to make sure practices were safe before trying them in people.

Obstacles now to germline engineering are practical, not theoretical. Scientists already have a way to add desired genes—snapping cassettes of them onto artificial chromosomes and injecting the chromosomes into newly fertilized eggs. Because every cell in the body is a descendant of that first fertilized egg, every cell would have a copy of the artificial chromosome.

Artificial chromosomes, even human artificial chromosomes, have been created and patented, the scientists reported, and companies have sprung up to exploit the technology.

Dr. Leroy Hood, the chairman of the department of molecular biotechnology at the University of Washington in Seattle, said he has developed a way to create an entire custom chromosome on a computer chip containing DNA.

But what if the artificial chromosome is faulty or what if it begins to look primitive to some future generation that wants the updated version of this genetic software? No problem, said Dr. Mario R. Capecchi, a distinguished professor of biology and human genetics at the University of Utah. Biologists already know how to make artificial chromosomes that can self destruct on command.

The lone ethicist speaking at the conference was Dr. John Fletcher, who was chief of bioethics at the National Institutes of Health and is now a professor of biomedical ethics at the University of Virginia. He said he had no problems in principle with giving people genes that would prevent or cure diseases.

But, he said, he is troubled by the idea of adding genes for certain complex traits. For example, he said, "somebody talked about genes for 'emotional stability.'" He said he finds this kind of talk problematic. However, he added, there is nothing intrinsically unethical about germline genetic engineering.

Scientists at the meeting also spoke quite seriously about extending the human life span with cassettes of anti-aging genes. And, they envisioned adding cassettes of anti-cancer genes and genes that would confer resistance to the AIDS virus. The cassettes would include control regions that would turn the genes on only in the tissues where and when needed.

Dr. Campbell described in detail how an anti-cancer gene cassette might work. He envisioned providing cells with the equivalent of a loaded gun, its trigger cocked. But the gun could only go off in certain cells and then only if a person deliberately pulled it. For prostate cancer, for example, scientists might add a gene that would kill prostate cells—and the cancer along with it—on command. To control such a gene, scientists would hook it to another gene that responds to an insect hormone, ecdysone, that normally has no effect on human cells.

If a man found he had prostate cancer, he would take an ecdysone pill. It would activate the added gene, killing prostate cells, but leaving other cells untouched.

The cassettes eventually could be enormously sophisticated, scientists said. If you wanted to enhance the human species, Dr. Hood explained, you would add entire clusters of genes that would interact and boost or modulate each other's effects like genes do in nature. The Human Genome Project, an ambitious effort to determine the sequence of human DNA, is going to find those gene clusters, he said. When that happens, he added, it will be "only a matter of time" before they are used in human germline engineering.

With the genome project, "we have the tools, the data, the vision, to do systems biology the way it was never done before," Dr. Hood said.

What is most amazing, said Dr. Lee Silver, a molecular geneticist at Princeton University and editor in chief of the journal *Mammalian Genome*, is that germline engineering, for a variety of technical reasons, should actually be easier than the more limited genetic engineering that scientists have tried thus far.

Dr. James D. Watson, director of the Cold Spring Harbor Laboratory in New York and winner of a Nobel Prize in 1962 for discovering the structure of DNA, agreed.

If scientists wait for conventional genetic engineering to succeed before trying germline engineering, Dr. Watson said, "We might as well wait for the sun to burn out."

And, he asked, why not try germline genetic engineering when the methods are ready? "If you could cure a very serious disease, stupidity, that would be a great thing for the people who otherwise would be born seriously disadvantaged."

Human in the Age
of Mechanical Reproduction

BY KAREN WRIGHT

"Mommy, where do babies come from?" Parents have dreaded this question ever since the stork made its first delivery; but today's mommies and daddies have more explaining to do than their own parents could possibly have imagined. Though the birds and bees discussion was never easy, its elements were fairly straightforward: the fireworks exploding, the train chugging through the tunnel, the waves pounding the shore, the occasional reference to anatomy. Once upon a time, baby-making was synonymous with whoopee-making, and frozen eggs were for pastry dough, and seven was how many times you should let the phone ring before you hang up, not how many fetuses you could fit in a womb.

These days, though, the facts of life can sound a lot like science fiction, as late-twentieth-century humanity grapples with the rise of noncoital conception. There are now more than a dozen ways to make a baby, the vast majority of which bypass the antiquated act of sexual congress. The last three decades have seen the advent of such high-tech interventions as fertility drugs, in vitro fertilization, donor eggs, donor sperm, donor embryos, and surrogate mothering. In the works are still more advanced technologies, such as the transfer of cell nuclei, embryo splitting, and even, if at least one man has his way, the cloning of human adults.

These techniques generally are gathered under the heading of "assisted reproduction." All the ones in use today were pioneered for and are usually employed by infertile couples of childbearing age. But they are also used by people with less conventional notions of parenting—singles, post-menopausal women, and gay partners. In the near future, assisted reproduction may become standard procedure for anyone who wants to conceive, and who can afford it. The allure, of course, is control: control over the timing of parenthood, control over "embryo quality," control over genetic disease, control over less pernicious characteristics, such as gender, that are also determined by genes.

So far, owing to federal policy and societal preference, the practice of assisted reproduction is largely unregulated. One specialist has even called it the Wild West of medicine. It's also expensive, bothersome, inefficient, and fraught with ethical complications—but none of those considerations has slowed its growth. Since 1978, when the first test-tube baby was born, the number of fertility clinics in the United States has gone from less than 30 to more than 300. The multibillion-dollar fertility industry has created tens of thousands of babies. Assisted reproduction has relieved the anguish of men and women who, just decades ago, would have had to abandon their hopes of having children. It's also created a world where a dead man can impregnate a stranger, where a woman can rent out her uterus, and where a child can have five parents—and still end up an orphan. It's not at all clear how this new world will change the meaning of family. But it has already transformed what used to be known as the miracle of birth.

Last November an Iowa couple made history, national television, and the covers of *Time* and *Newsweek* when their seven babies were born alive. "We're trusting in God," the McCaugheys told reporters when asked how they would cope with the sudden surfeit of offspring. But to conceive for the second time, Bobbi McCaughey had trusted in Metrodin, a fertility drug that stimulates the ripening of eggs in the ovaries. A woman on Metrodin can produce dozens of eggs in a month instead of just one.

...

Even so, taking fertility drugs is not like taking aspirin. Most are administered by daily injections that couples are trained to perform....

And there are risks. The most common is multiple pregnancy: the simultaneous conception of two or (many) more fetuses, like the McCaugheys'. Despite the celebratory atmosphere that greeted the Iowa septuplets, such pregnancies are in fact a grave predicament for would-be parents. Multiple pregnancies increase the odds of maternal complications such as high blood pressure and diabetes. And they pose even greater risks for the unborn. The fetuses gestating in a multiple pregnancy are far more susceptible than their single peers to miscarriage, birth defects, low birth weight, and premature birth, as well as lifelong problems that can result from prematurity—including cerebral palsy, blindness, kidney failure, and mental retardation.

... Whereas in the general population the rate of multiple pregnancy is 1 to 2 percent, the rate among women treated with fertility drugs can be as high as 25 percent.

...

IVF [in vitro fertilization] is the cornerstone of assisted reproductive technology. The procedure—in which ripe eggs are removed from the ovaries and incubated with sperm—greatly improves the haphazard gambit of traditional in vivo fertilization....

...

... [H]owever, the efficacy of assisted reproduction is sobering.... Success rates for IVF depend on a patient's age and vary from clinic to clinic and from procedure to procedure. But the ballpark figure—the so-called take-home baby rate—is one live birth for every five IVF cycles. Infertility specialists point out that the success rates for these procedures increase every year and that in any given month a fertile couple's chance of conceiving by traditional means is also one in five. According to the American Society for Reproductive Medicine, more than half of all infertile couples could attain pregnancy if they persisted long enough with treatments for assisted reproduction.

But that also means that about half will never have a baby, no matter how much therapy they get. And one thing about making babies by the usual means is that it's free. If at first you don't succeed, you can try, try again, without taking out a second mortgage. A single cycle of IVF, on the other hand, costs between $8,000 and $10,000....

Is it worth it? The market says yes. Although rates of infertility have remained constant, demand for infertility services has risen steadily in the past two decades. Today about 6 million couples in the United States have fertility problems; half of them go to their doctors for help, and about a quarter end up trying assisted reproduction....

...

Moreover, pursuing parenthood via assisted reproduction means being confronted with ethical decisions well outside the range of most people's moral radars. Because IVF techniques often give rise to multiple pregnancies, selective reduction is an issue here as well. Couples undergoing IVF must also decide how many eggs to fertilize and transfer at one time (which bears on the question of multiple pregnancy), whether they want to create and freeze embryos for future use, and what the eventual disposition of any unused frozen embryos should be. Former spouses have waged custody battles over frozen embryos, and in at least one case the attending IVF clinic claimed the embryo as its lawful property. Legally, human embryos occupy a gray area all their own, somewhere between human life and some rarefied form of property.

Assisted reproduction also invites the preselection of embryos based on genetic traits, and all the moral dilemmas that may accrue thereto. Screening is done by removing a single cell from an eight-cell embryo and analyzing the chromosomes or DNA in the cell nucleus. Already some clinics offer to screen in vitro embryos for genes related to cystic fibrosis, hemophilia, and muscular dystrophy. Couples can decide which of the embryos they've created meet their specifications; the rejected embryos can be discarded or donated to research.

Finally, assisted reproduction has opened the door to all manner of gamete swapping and surrogacy, from the simplest and oldest method—artificial insemination with a donor's sperm—to more complex scenarios in which any combination of donor eggs, donor sperm, and donor embryos may be used. In addition to biological surrogate motherhood (the method that created the celebrated Baby M), "gestational surrogates" will agree to carry and give birth to a baby to whom they bear no genetic relation whatsoever. It is now possible for a person to "have" a baby by procuring eggs and sperm from donors and hiring a "birth mother" to do the rest (this has been done). It is possible for a woman to use a birth mother for cosmetic reasons or convenience alone (this has also been done). It is possible for the sperm of dead men to be retrieved and used to impregnate their widows (likewise). It is possible for women long past the age of menopause to give birth (this, too, has already happened).

...

... Once it becomes widely available, cryopreservation will offer a unique opportunity to women: the chance to store their young eggs for use at a later date. Defects in aging eggs are thought to be responsible for the declining fertility of older women; indeed, donor-egg technology has demonstrated that the rest of the female reproductive apparatus withstands the test of time. By assuring women a lifetime of viable gametes, egg freezing could let them beat the biological clock.

...

A striking example comes from the laboratory of reproductive endocrinologist Jamie Grifo at New York University Medical Center. In another effort to beat the biological clock, Grifo is transferring the nuclei from older women's eggs into younger eggs from which the nuclei have been removed—that is, enucleated eggs. When these hybrid cells are artificially stimulated to divide, the transferred nuclei don't show the chromosomal abnormalities typical of vintage eggs. Grifo's work is still in the research stage, but he hopes eventually to fertilize such eggs and implant them in his patients.

Grifo is not cloning humans, but his experiments draw on established mammalian cloning technology. Lamb 6LL3, better known as Dolly, was created by nuclear transfer from an adult cell to an enucleated egg.... "But the fact is, [cloning humans is] possible," he says. "I just can't think of any clinical indications for it."

If Grifo can't, someone else can. Richard Seed, a physicist turned infertility entrepreneur, made headlines in January when he announced that he was seeking funds to establish a laboratory for the cloning of adult human beings.

The National Bioethics Advisory Commission recommended a ban on human cloning back when Dolly first saw daylight.... But the American Society for Reproductive Medicine, which issues ethical guidelines for the use of assisted-reproduction technologies, has taken the middle ground. "We do not support the cloning of an existing—or previously existing—individual," says Younger. "But that is not to say that cloning technology is bad." Cultures of cloned nerve cells, for example, could be used to treat spinal-cord injuries, he says. "We would not like to see research curtailed."

The society has also come out in favor of continuing research on embryo "twinning"—a procedure, done so far only in animals, in which a single embryo is divided to create two genetically identical individuals. The society's rationale is that the technique of embryo twinning could provide infertile couples with twice as many embryos to implant. But the distinction between cloning and twinning grows obscure if say, one of the twinned embryos is frozen until its sibling has grown to adulthood.

Critics of assisted reproduction fear that today's innovations will become tomorrow's imperatives....

And lack of regulation only exacerbates the problems surrounding assisted reproduction. "This field is screaming for regulation, oversight, and control," says Arthur Caplan, a noted bioethicist at the University of Pennsylvania. "What keeps us from doing so is the notion that individuals should have procreative freedom."

...

Specialists in assisted reproduction, including Grifo, say ... that regulators wouldn't appreciate the technical and moral complexities of the work. But with the bulk of experimentation going on in private clinics, patients—and their children—can become guinea pigs. Even when couples are not directly involved in experimental procedures, they may be confronted with uncomfortable choices, such as financial incentives to donate their gametes or embryos.

...

And market forces affect more than just infertile couples.... [I]n February the *New York Times* reported that St. Barnabas Medical Center, a fertility clinic in Livingston, New Jersey, has begun offering young women $5,000 to donate eggs.... Unlike payment for organs, which is illegal, limited payment for eggs is legal. The professional guidelines of the American Society for Reproductive Medicine deem them "body products," not "body parts."

Many observers fear that it is not the participants in assisted reproduction but their children who may suffer most from the imprudent use of these new technologies. For example, with the rising popularity of assisted reproduction, more and more children are being exposed to the risks of premature birth: Since 1971 the annual number of multiple births in the United States has more than quadrupled. Scientists and ethicists alike have spoken out against helping single, postmenopausal mothers conceive, arguing that it is morally reprehensible to create children who may well be orphaned. Some question the wisdom of arrangements—like surrogacy or gamete donation—that could diffuse the responsibility of parenthood.... A recent—and controversial—Australian study of 420 children suggests that babies produced with the aid of intracytoplasmic sperm injection, in which a single sperm is injected into an incubating egg cell, are twice as likely to suffer major birth defects of the heart, genitals, and digestive tract.

"Everything we do in vitro to a mammalian embryo causes it stress," says Robert Edwards, the specialist who presided over the first test-tube baby 20 years ago. "But there's immense responsibility in the scientific community" to evaluate and eliminate any adverse consequences of new procedures, he says.

...

With the rapid advances in assisted-reproduction techniques, the ethical and legal issues can only become more complicated, and the task of resolving them will fall to future generations. But that may be fitting, if it's the children of assisted reproduction who pass judgment on the technology that helped create them.